Toward Understanding Administrators
in the Medical Environment

FRANCES M. TAPPAN, Ed. D.

*Professor, Assistant Dean, and Director of the
Academic Program, School of Physical Therapy,
University of Connecticut, Storrs*

TOWARD UNDERSTANDING ADMINISTRATORS IN THE MEDICAL ENVIRONMENT

RA972
T174t
1968

THE MACMILLAN COMPANY, NEW YORK
COLLIER-MACMILLAN LIMITED, LONDON

First Printing

Library of Congress catalog card number: 68-12287

THE MACMILLAN COMPANY, NEW YORK
COLLIER-MACMILLAN CANADA, LTD., TORONTO, ONTARIO

PRINTED IN THE UNITED STATES OF AMERICA

To all those very special people who are sincerely devoted to good patient-centered care

Foreword

The pursuit of harmonious, peaceful, and effective administration depends in large measure on administrative leadership as well as respectful understanding from those receiving direction.

The author of this book has endeavored to present the basic, essential tools which will assist the professional employee in many health fields in appreciating administrators and problems of administration as well as the importance of leadership in the solution of these problems. It has been Dr. Tappan's hope that destructive criticism of administrators will be replaced by a sincere and genuine desire to understand why certain administrative decisions are made and the rationale behind the decisions.

The aim of this book is good patient-centered care through a cooperative team approach. Content develops in response to carefully stated questions. Case studies furnish an enrichment for both the student and faculty member pursuing a deeper awareness of administration and the need for multidisciplinary collaboration.

Dr. Tappan's many years of experience as an employee in a general hospital and her sixteen years of administration, which included the teaching and guiding of collegiate students in the principles of administration, as well as her doctoral work at Teacher's College of Columbia University, have provided her with a wealth of information for this book.

JOSEPHINE A. DOLAN
Professor of Nursing
University of Connecticut
Storrs, Connecticut

Preface

Many books analyze the principles and practices of administration in the medical environment, but few books tell the employee what the administrator is trying to accomplish.

Part I discusses the employee's relationships with the many persons in various administrative positions throughout the medical institution. It examines and analyzes who administrators are and what they do. It answers the many questions which confront employees or students preparing to work in the medical environment. It gives full consideration to the ethical, legal, and moral issues which influence administrative decisions. It discusses, also, the components that will lead employees toward the realization that understanding of the self leads to improved relations with co-workers, patients, and administrators.

Part II consists of cases for study and discussion which illustrate again and again that administrators who are well aware of their responsibilities find it practically impossible to accomplish their administrative goals because of innumerable frustrations and unexpected developments.

This book addresses itself to students of all medical disciplines. It will serve as a valuable guide to employees already working in hospitals or other medical services such as rehabilitation centers and extended care facilities.

F. M. T.

Acknowledgments

My deep appreciation is expressed to Josephine A. Dolan for her advice and counsel, which assured, in particular, the accuracy of the administrative problems related to nursing. Credit should be given to the National Foundation (formerly the National Foundation for Infantile Paralysis) for its financial support in the education which prepared the author to write this book. Acknowledgment is expressed to Professor Eleanor Lambertsen and Professor Walter Sindlinger for their combined efforts to make the dissertation from which this book developed as accurate and as well organized as possible.

Appreciation is expressed to the students of the School of Physical Therapy and the School of Nursing at the University of Connecticut for their interest and cooperation in gathering the case material for Part II of this book. Words cannot express my gratitude to my family for their constant faith, moral support, and patience.

I owe thanks to E. Alice Beard, Ed.D., for reading and editing this manuscript.

I am also deeply indebted to Virginia Darrow, who faithfully typed this book, often working far into the night to meet numerous deadlines.

I would like to thank Mr. Henry Van Swearingen, Editor, College and Professional Division, The Macmillan Company, without whose encouragement I would never have become an author.

Contents

ADMINISTRATORS AND ADMINISTRATION

Chapter 1

Introduction

Today's modern hospital is becoming increasingly complex, making it more difficult for the beginning employee to understand his role in the total organization. The hospital, with all of its equipment and special facilities, is basically an organization of people who operate the equipment and perform the multitude of services necessary for the hospital to function effectively. The new employee must find out how he fits into the organization, to whom he is responsible, and what his own particular duties are.

The new employee may be a well-prepared individual in such a specialized field as physical therapy. But in the process of familiarizing himself with his new duties he soon discovers that there are many things he needs to know about the hospital in which he is to work. He needs to know something about administration and the administrative organization. He needs to know the operational policies and the ethical and legal controls under which he will operate. He needs to know the importance of verbal and written communication. He needs to know something about human relations. Above all, he needs to understand his own unique contribution toward the achievement of the goals of the organization.

Unfortunately, because of the shortage of personnel and the urgent need to attend to the tasks at hand, proper orientation for new employees is not always provided. In many instances, new employees, if they are interested at all, must find out for themselves the answers to the questions about the organization and administration of their hospitals.

PURPOSE

The purpose of this book is to provide instructional material that can be used to assist in orienting new employees to the hospital setting in which they will work. This instructional material consists of (1) cases that were developed from reports of situations written by students and young personnel working in medical institutions for the first time, (2) instructions for the use of the cases, and (3) background information concerning administration that can be used to help students become familiar with the hospital setting in which they will work and provide background information to facilitate discussion of the cases. It is hoped that this book will help young people to better prepare themselves to work responsibly with dignity and self-respect and will aid them in their transition from student to professional worker.

LIMITATIONS

A book such as this has certain definite limitations. First of all, it is not intended to be a detailed and comprehensive book on hospital administration. It is designed to introduce students and recent graduates of medically related professional schools to the complex organization of the modern hospital and the kinds of problems they may encounter on the job. Obviously, some areas included in the background section of this book will need more intensive coverage; a variety of textbooks and references are included in the bibliography.

The intent of this book is to provide general orientation material only. Orientation to each specific medical facility is still essential.

DEVELOPMENT OF CASE MATERIALS

The first step in the development of cases for this book was to devise an instrument that would assist persons to write actual incidents that had been encountered in their first contacts with medical personnel from which the cases could be developed. These persons included junior students experiencing early exposure to the clinical environment in the School of Physical Therapy and the School of Nursing at the University of Connecticut. The same instrument was given to experienced nurses, x-ray technicians, doctors, dietitians, hospital administrators, and patients who cooperated in the collection of cases.

INSTRUCTIONS FOR WRITING ADMINISTRATIVE CASE STUDIES

1. Describe the basic type of institution in which the incident occurred.

2. Describe the type of department in which it occurred. Was it specialized, such as a children's hospital or a rehabilitation center? Was it a general hospital?

3. Describe the administrative atmosphere. Did it help or hinder your ability to function as a practitioner? Include the necessary background of the individuals involved, their personality and personal as well as professional background.

4. Tell the story. Describe the incident. Diagram the channels of authority showing:
   a. At what level in chain of command this incident became a problem.
   b. From there trace the causes of the incident.
   c. From there trace the effects of this incident.

5. Do not analyze the situation in writing the case but on separate pages discuss:

a. What could have been done to prevent this from developing?

b. What could or should have been done at the time?

c. What basic administrative or ethical changes could be made to improve the relationships existing in the department described?

The reason for collection of the case material was given by the author to all involved. It was explained that the purpose of the collection of incidents and cases was to identify questions related to administrative problems facing the new employee that could be organized into cases which could be used for discussion in classes for people planning to work in medical institutions.

Over a four-year period, a review of the literature continued and 357 cases and critical incidents were collected. These cases came from many different types of medical institutions including general hospitals, veterans' hospitals, army hospitals, institutions for the mentally retarded, schools of nursing, and other related fields such as cerebral palsy centers and homes for the chronically ill. Analysis of cases and incidents was continued until the material began to repeat itself and no significant additions were identified.

From these situations 21 composite cases were written which integrated the most common incidents met by young people. In all cases names of individuals and hospitals were changed to avoid embarrassing any particular medical facility. Frequent conferences were held with leaders in the field who could identify questions and who could react to cases and questions already prepared. Incidents seldom referred to in the literature were eliminated.

The written cases were tested in classroom situations to identify those that stimulated the most active discussion. After cases were discussed in class, the cases were rewritten to add necessary information and to clarify certain points that had caused confusion in the class discussions. Cases that did not stimulate active discussion were eliminated.

IDENTIFICATION OF KEY QUESTIONS

The process of exploring the literature, studying the cases prepared by students and workers in the hospital setting, and conferring with students and hospital personnel led to the identification of the following questions for which a new worker should have some answers before he can function properly.

1. What is administration?
2. What are the functions of administration?
3. How does administration function in the medical environment?
4. What is a hospital?
5. What kinds of hospitals are there?
6. What services do hospitals perform?
7. What kinds of departments are there in a hospital to perform these services?
8. Who else is involved in patient-centered care?
9. How did administration develop in hospitals?
10. Who is legally responsible for the operation of the hospital?
11. What are the functions of the board?
12. How does the board operate?
13. Who is the hospital administrator?
14. Why is it necessary to have a hospital administrator?
15. What does a hospital administrator do?
16. What is the medical staff of the hospital?
17. How does the medical staff function?
18. What are the relationships between the medical staff and the trustees, the hospital administrator, and medical as well as institutional services?
19. Why is it necessary to know about codes of ethics?
20. Why do the various medical specialties need codes of ethics?

21. How can ethical decisions be made?
22. What are some of the legal controls needed in the medical environment?
23. Why are licenses necessary?
24. What are contracts?
25. What is breach of contract?
26. What is malpractice?
27. What is negligence?
28. What is liability?
29. What is meant by the "inner self"?
30. What is meant by susceptibility to environment?
31. How can one foster self-development?
32. What are favorable and unfavorable responses?
33. Why does impersonality often exist?
34. Why is it necessary to work well with co-workers?

At the same time the composite cases were being prepared, the questions and incidents identified were analyzed in order to develop material that could be used to introduce students to the medical environment, to provide answers to some of the more common questions raised, and to prepare them for the use of the case studies.

ORGANIZATION

Part I of this book discusses questions concerned with administration in the hospital. It states the growth and development of administrative policies and describes patterns of organization that exist in the majority of institutions. Ethical and legal influences are considered and the employee's relationships with the many people in various administrative positions throughout the medical institution are explained.

Part II presents cases that involve the questions discussed in Part I. Each case is related to one or more administrative incidents in the medical environment.

Chapter 2

The Nature of Administration

WHAT IS ADMINISTRATION?

To begin to develop an understanding of administrators it is necessary first to understand what administration *is* and why it is necessary.

The word administration is derived from the Latin word *administrare*, meaning "to attend, manage, to serve." [1] Thus administration signifies service. The process of administration involves planning, organizing, directing, coordinating, and evaluating the activities of an organization so that the associated efforts of the group who make up the organization can be achieved.

Any group working together must have leadership. The group needs people at the top level who will give direction to the organization and who will determine what policies are needed to achieve the goals of the organization. The group also needs people close to its own tasks who understand its immediate situation and who can coordinate its activities.

The instant a leader is elected, selected, or appointed the process of administration begins. Historically, as soon as men were aware that certain objectives could be more completely realized

[1] *Webster's Third International Dictionary.* Springfield, Massachusetts: G. and C. Merriam Co., 1966.

through group effort, leadership was created and rudimentary administrative functions developed. Early human associations that brought large numbers of people into action together were military bodies and the church.[2]

Administrators are responsible for what the institution is expected to accomplish—how it will organize; how it will select its staff and physical facilities; how it will delegate responsibility and authority; how it will conduct its programs and modify them in light of experience; and how it will build and maintain the morale of all its personnel, since all personnel are a part of the organization and all participate in it in varying ways and degrees.[3]

The larger and more complex the organization becomes, the more difficult it is for individuals performing their own necessary tasks to understand administration. Every institution has its own unique administrative needs and will therefore use varying methods of organization. No one explanation of what administration *is* can completely define administration in all of its complexity. Tead describes it as the concrete effort to direct, guide, and integrate associated human strivings that are focused toward some specific ends or aims.[4] Simon states that administration is concerned with the processes of decision making as well as with the processes of action.[5] Hungate discusses administration in terms of functions, stating that the administrator plans, programs, budgets, makes expenditures, assigns staff, provides supervision, and is continually involved in evaluation.[6]

[2] Ordway Tead. *The Art of Administration.* New York: McGraw-Hill Book Co., Inc., 1951, p. 2.

[3] Thad L. Hungate. *Management in Higher Education.* New York: Bureau of Publication, Teachers College, Columbia University, 1964, p. 63.

[4] Tead, *op. cit.,* p. 3.

[5] Herbert A. Simon. *Administrative Behavior.* New York: The Macmillan Co., 1958, p. 1.

[6] Hungate, *op. cit.,* p. 111.

WHAT ARE THE FUNCTIONS OF ADMINISTRATION?

The major function of administration is to get the required job done with the least possible expenditure of time, money, and energy.[7] Administration is concerned with accomplishment of defined objectives. The science of administration is the system of knowledge whereby those responsible for the organization may understand relationships, predict results, and influence outcomes in any situation where men are organized at work together for a common purpose.

Examination of the many books dealing with general administration suggests that there are basically 11 major functions of administration.

1. Development of Organizational Plans

It is a function of administration to develop plans and establish long-term goals for the structuring of the organization. There is a constant need to recruit and organize capable staff that can work together as a team, concerned with the over-all objectives of the organization rather than being primarily interested in individual goals.

2. Grouping of Related Activities

It is a function of administration to group related activities and assure leadership by appointing assistant administrators. By appointing these assistants, the chief administrative officer is relieved of much of the routine work and is free to unite the efforts of the various groups. Administration must provide these subgroups with adequate equipment and personnel to realize their individual goals.

[7] Luther Gulick and Lyndall Urwick (eds.). *Papers on the Science of Administration.* New York: Institute of Public Administration, 1937, p. 191.

3. Delegation of Responsibility and Authority

It is a function of administration to delegate responsibility and give authority to those leaders who will be in charge of the various units or departments of the organization. Once such responsibilities have been delegated, it is the function of administration to follow through and see that things are running smoothly. This is done by holding conferences with the various unit leaders at all levels to achieve coordination among all departments of the organization. This results in more efficient coordination and reduces friction between departments or within departments.

4. Development of Policies

It is the directive function of administration to develop policies that include both institutional objectives and the plans to achieve them. These policies are reviewed and modified to accommodate new conditions or procedures that may develop.[8] These directive policies provide a basis for action.

5. Resolving Conflicts

It is a function of administration to assist members of the organization in finding solutions to problems that may interfere with the work of the organization.

6. Making Decisions

Certain situations can be promptly taken care of by a firm decision based on existing policy. At other times, especially where over-all policies are being revised, there may be a lag between the time the policy change is decided upon and is implemented. Therefore, it is a function of administration to review existing policies and to modify them if necessary.

7. Development of Long-Range Plans

It is a function of administration to anticipate the changing needs of society and in light of this to forecast future needs and trends and seek ways and means of realizing them.

[8] Hungate, *op. cit.*, p. 68.

8. Maintaining Lines of Communication

It is a function of administration to maintain open channels of communication so that information may flow freely in all directions: upward so that department heads may keep top administration alert to their immediate needs; downward so that boards of directors and chief administrators can make it possible for these needs to be met; and horizontally so that what is decided will come to the attention of all who may be affected by the decision. In this way employees can all be kept informed.

9. Development of Personnel

It is a function of administration to assure development of all personnel involved in any aspect of the program. One way to encourage this feeling of individual self-respect is for administration to seek ideas from groups and individuals so that every employee feels his contribution is appreciated.

10. Maintenance of High Morale

It is a function of administration to keep morale high, energizing and stimulating all personnel and giving full recognition to new ideas and for a job well done. Organizations differ in the way they function even though they deal with the same product. Personalities differ and the administrative approach must lend itself to finding the best way to accomplish solutions for the many problems that arise. No ideal method of administration can be described that will be useful in all situations.

11. The Provisions of Strong Leadership

Democracy in administration is desirable, but it has its limits and there are times when strong leadership must be exerted and decisions must be made. If confusion exists among or between groups of assistant administrators and their personnel, the confusion must be resolved. If administration is to succeed, it must have leadership with integrity and simple, basic honesty.

HOW DOES ADMINISTRATION FUNCTION IN THE MEDICAL ENVIRONMENT?

Administration of a medical facility is much like administration in any other organization. Only the goals are different. In a medical facility the primary objective is good patient-centered care rather than a product.

The functions of administration in the medical environment vary greatly according to the roles of the many medical specialists involved. Each classification of administrators and assistant administrators has a specific number of tasks that fall logically into units for purposes of execution. Under these circumstances administrative patterns must, of necessity, grow out of a definition of the activities to be performed and in light of selected personnel who will perform them. These patterns must also consider four basic needs:

1. The Need for Close Cooperation

There must be close cooperation and teamwork among the many medical specialties that work together in medical facilities. Medical knowledge has exploded to the point that no one man can, within one life-span, know more than a small fraction of it. Therefore, the work must be divided according to the nature, capacity, and skill of those involved. To keep the patient as the center of the organization objectives is perhaps one of the most important purposes of administration in the medical situation. (See Fig. 1.) Hospitalized patients are all people with problems, and often the slightest mistake can increase their physical or psychologic difficulties.

2. The Need to Function Effectively

There is a greater need for an administrative median by which all the many medical and nonmedical departments can interact harmoniously and function effectively as an integrated part of a

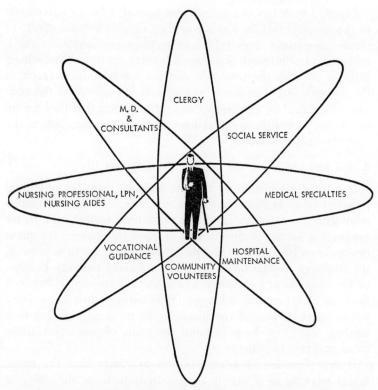

FIGURE 1. *Relationship of administrative units and related services.*

large organization. Psychologic as well as physical welfare of patients is of major concern to the over-all administration of medical facilities. Patients who already are worried and upset by personal problems are supersensitive to their immediate environment and more easily upset by little things which become very important to them. It is important for administration to have at the top of its objectives the organization of departments that will operate harmoniously and smoothly and that will give the patient the feeling of confidence he needs to know that he is getting the best of care.

Figure 1 indicates in a simple way how all administrative units in the medical facility overlap as they revolve around efforts to serve the patient. Some of these services are strictly medical; others are institutional. Some even involve "outsiders" who have little to do with the total administrative organization (such as the clergy). But even these people need to understand the policies established by administration and to realize that they are an important part of the organization and that they contribute to the patients total treatment.

3. The Need to Value the Importance of Human Life

In a medical institution the presence of many ill or injured people unable to care for themselves necessitates conscientious administration to assure good and continuous patient care. If, for instance, a factory suffers a loss of electrical power, the plant closes down for the day. If a power failure occurs in a hospital, the stoppage of vital facilities endangers many patients. Patients on their way to or from surgery or obstetrics are caught between floors in elevators and lights go out in surgery. Just as auxiliary power must be part of the planning, so must all planning in a medical institution keep in mind the goals of protection, treatment, and care of patients.

It is a function of administration to assure that the many teams working in a variety of situations to serve the different purposes of specialized departments realize they do not function as individual teams, but that their work involves and affects other people and other teams. The dietitian's team may prepare the food perfectly, but if delays in delivery occur, the food may be delivered cold, or if a nurse or aide delivers it to the wrong patient, the results planned by the team are in vain.

4. The Need to Consider the Patient

Although administrators are seldom the ones actually working with patients it is their function to assure the highest quality of care possible, considering the patient's physical and emotional environment as well as his bodily care. The patient must be made to feel that he is *the* person around whom the whole hospital functions. Its purpose is to be of service to him. All patients find themselves uprooted from their daily ways of life during their hospital stay, and their disorientation is compounded by their illness, pain, and discomfort. Administrative planning must try to maintain some continuity with the patient's accustomed pattern of living.

It would be humanly impossible for busy administrators who are primarily concerned with coordinating the activities of personnel to be aware of all patient needs. These needs can be met more easily through the therapeutic effectiveness of architectural design, effective use of personnel, and recent techniques of noise elimination such as soundproof ceilings and the use of transistor call sets carried by the doctor.

SUMMARY

The process of administration involves planning, organizing, directing, coordinating, and evaluating the activities of an organization so that the associated efforts of the personnel making up the organization can be achieved.

Administrators are responsible for what the institution is expected to accomplish—how it will organize, how it will select its staff and physical facilities, how it will delegate responsibility and authority, how it will conduct its programs and modify them in light of experience, and how it will build and maintain the morale of all its personnel.

The functions of administration are to—

1. Develop organizational plans
2. Group related activities
3. Delegate responsibility of authority
4. Develop policies
5. Resolve conflicts
6. Make decisions

7. Develop long-range plans
8. Maintain lines of communication
9. Develop personnel
10. Maintain high morale
11. Provide strong leadership

To accomplish this, four basic needs must be recognized:

1. The need for close cooperation
2. The need to function effectively
3. The need to value the importance of human life
4. The need to consider the patient

Chapter 3 will discuss the hospital setting, explaining what a hospital is, what kinds there are, and the services they provide.

Bibliography

Gulick, Luther, and Lyndall Urwick (eds.). *Papers on the Science of Administration*. New York: Institute of Public Administration, 1937.

Hungate, Thad L. *Management in Higher Education*. New York: Bureau of Publications, Teachers College, Columbia University, 1964.

Simon, Herbert A. *Administrative Behavior*. New York: The Macmillan Co., 1958.

Tead, Ordway. *The Art of Administration*. New York: McGraw-Hill Book Co., Inc., 1951.

Webster's Third International Dictionary. Springfield, Mass.: G. and C. Merriam Co., 1966.

The Hospital Setting

WHAT IS A HOSPITAL?

A hospital consists of a building or group of buildings, space, equipment, skilled people, and patients. The modern hospital provides medical, surgical, pediatric, and obstetric services to patients who require nursing care. In addition, many hospitals provide rehabilitative and psychiatric care. These same services may also be available to the public on an outpatient basis. Through a hospital's outpatient department much of the equipment too expensive for individuals to afford is provided for the use of society.

Hospitals serve four distinct functions: the care of the sick, public and professional education, the conduction of research, and preventive medicine.[1]

WHAT KINDS OF HOSPITALS ARE THERE?

Hospitals can be classified as voluntary, government, and proprietary.[2] Sloan describes the voluntary hospital as a "public

[1] Raymond P. Sloan. *This Hospital Business of Ours.* New York: G. P. Putnam's Sons, 1952, p. 3.

[2] Raymond P. Sloan. *Today's Hospital.* New York: Harper and Row, 1966, p. 3.

enterprise conducted under private management, sponsored by boards of men and women representative of the community who are legally and morally responsible for its professional services, properties and policies." [3] He also explains that government hospitals are supported by tax funds and are sponsored by federal, state, city, or county bodies. Sloan describes proprietary hospitals as those operated for profit, frequently financed by doctors or other individuals who desire the advantages of greater independence.

Hospitals may also be classified as *general* or *special*.[4] The general hospital provides care for all types of cases, whereas the special hospital may concentrate on the treatment of children, tuberculosis, mental disorders, and so forth. Whatever the type of hospital it is, good patient care is the primary objective.

WHAT SERVICES DO HOSPITALS PERFORM?

Hospitals of all kinds are primarily designed for patient-centered care. *Medical services* include medical and nursing services. They also include such specialized departments as the laboratory, x-ray service, pharmacy, social service, operating room, medical dietary, physical therapy, occupational therapy, and speech therapy.

Employees involved in *institutional services* include such people as maintenance men for buildings and grounds, housekeepers, laundry workers, electricians, plumbers, carpenters, painters, and mechanics. Financial details need to be taken care of by people in accounting, credit, payroll, and purchasing. When one considers the payroll, cost of operation, purchasing department, number of employees, and the various service departments the hospital must maintain, the total annual cost of a large hospital's operations ranges in the millions. Other services

3 *Ibid.*, p. 4.
4 *Ibid.*, p. 7.

include central supply, medical records, admitting, nonmedical dietary, secretarial, and volunteer workers.

If all these services are not coordinated, poor patient care can result. If any of the workers do not bear in mind the total purpose of the hospital, problems leading to poor patient care can arise. For example, if the maintenance department polishes the floors too highly, patients or staff may fall, causing injuries.

WHAT KINDS OF DEPARTMENTS ARE THERE IN A HOSPITAL TO PERFORM THESE SERVICES?

Hospitals have a complex organization composed of many departments. All departments include people who have the unified purpose of caring for the sick and the injured. No two institutions will follow the same pattern of organization.

Patterns of hospital administration develop out of the needs of a particular hospital at a particular time. New departments may be established in response to demands for new services; some departments may disappear.

Throughout this process some consistent pattern of organization is necessary. Various people from the board of directors through the hospital administrator and the medical staff and down to all the department heads are constantly making decisions that affect the total administration of the medical institution.

It is the responsibility of the board of directors to see that the purposes and policies are carried out. The board hires a person usually called the hospital administrator. He may also be given the title of president or vice-president.

It is the responsibility of this administrator to coordinate all the activities of the institution, both medical and nonmedical. He works through a joint conference committee consisting of members of the medical staff and the board of directors with the administrator serving as an ex officio member. This joint conference committee coordinates the activities of the medical staff, the board of directors, and the hospital administrator. According to Sloan, joint conference committees may appear under other titles such as "Medical Advisory Committee" or "Committee of Professional and Medical Affairs." [5] Regardless of title these committees meet, report, and make recommendations to the board that affect the pattern of organization of the medical staff. They also work with other committees such as finance, building, and development committees.

The medical staff is composed of doctors who use the facilities of a medical institution. In most cases they are not employed or paid by the hospital, yet they work a large percentage of their time within the hospital.

Doctors in charge of pathology, physical therapy, x-ray, and other specialized departments are usually employed by the hospital, but they are also members of the medical staff.

Most medical staffs are self-governing, having their own constitution and bylaws. The medical staff elects its officers after which the board approves of their appointment. Attendance at medical staff meetings is usually compulsory. This group meets as often as once a week to decide on policy within its own group.

The medical staff is in contact with many departments of the hospital. When the doctor gives orders to hospital personnel as he plans for treatment of his patients, he is assuming a therapeutic function. A physician may not delegate the authority to diagnose, to treat, or to prescribe, but he does delegate to the members of the health team certain areas of responsibility. Increasingly, certain therapeutic measures previously conceived to be the responsibility of the physician are delegated by him to some other person.

Working closely with the doctor, the nurses are of prime importance in providing patient-centered care. Because nursing service includes a great majority of the people who work in the hospital, their function should be clearly understood.

[5] *Ibid.*, p. 37.

The *director of nursing* [6] or assistant administrator for nursing is a registered professional nurse who has the full authority and responsibility for the administration of nursing services to individuals and families in a health care facility or an organized group of health care facilities.

The *associate director of nursing* is a registered professional nurse who works in a cooperative and consultative relationship with the director and assumes primary delegated responsibilities in the administration of nursing services to individuals and families in a health care facility or an organized group of health care facilities.

The *assistant director of nursing* is a registered professional nurse who assumes responsibilities for specific functions as delegated by the director and/or the associate director in the administration of nursing services to individuals and families within a health care facility or an organized group of health care facilities.

The responsibilities of the administrators of nursing service are to plan, organize, direct, coordinate, and evaluate the activities of the nursing department. These responsibilities include the functions identified below.[7]

1. Develops a written philosophy and objectives for the nursing department which are compatible with the purpose of the health care facility.

a. Provides for the participation of staff members in developing and revising the philosophy and the objectives.

b. Develops a plan for communicating the philosophy and the objectives to all members to determine the manner in which the philosophy and objectives will be used to guide the nursing service program.

c. Communicates and interprets the philosophy and ob-

[6] American Nurses' Association. *Statement of Functions and Qualifications for Nursing Service Administrators.* New York: American Nurses' Association, August, 1966, p. 2.

[7] *Ibid.,* p. 3.

jectives and their implementation to administration, the medical staff, and other appropriate departments.

2. Establishes and implements standards which insure safe and therapeutically effective nursing care of patients.

a. Provides for the participation of staff members in the formulation of the nursing care standards.

b. Makes provisions for all members of the nursing service to know the standards and their personal responsibility in upholding them.

c. Establishes a plan by which each patient's nursing care is planned, given or supervised, and evaluated by a professional nurse.

3. Develops nursing service policies which focus on the care of the patient, favor the practice of nursing, and help attract and retain qualified nursing service personnel.

4. Participates in the establishment and promotion of administrative policies and practices which favor the practice of nursing and provide a climate which helps nursing personnel to increase their professional, technical, and psychosocial skills.

5. Participates in reviewing and revising the personnel policies of the health care facility and establishes criteria and procedures for the recruitment, selection, promotion, and termination of employment of nursing personnel.

6. Establishes the functions and qualifications for each nursing position.

7. Determines a staffing plan which will accomplish the stated objectives and standards of the nursing services and promotes the maximum utilization of all nursing personnel.

8. Directs the nursing personnel and the activities of the nursing department.

9. Organizes the nursing department to delineate authority, functional responsibilities, lines of relationship, and communication to provide safe and therapeutically effective nursing care.

10. Evaluates nursing care and the climate in which it is practiced to identify achievements and problems, and to provide data for forecasting and planning.

11. Develops and maintains an effective system of nursing records and reports.

12. Collaborates with the administrative staff, other department personnel and representatives of allied groups in planning for coordinated services to patients.

13. Provides for nursing personnel to plan with the medical staff and other patient care disciplines for the total needs of patients.

14. Participates in the assessment of community health care resources for provision of continuity of care for patients within the agency, on discharge, and on referral to another health or nursing care facility.

15. Determines and recommends a departmental budget to implement stated objectives.
   a. Makes provision for personnel, supplies, and equipment necessary to meet nursing needs of patients.
   b. Provides for orientation and inservice educational needs of nursing personnel.

16. Controls and evaluates the allocated budget for adequacy for the present and the future.

17. Plans with representatives of administration and other appropriate groups for the development of new and the effective use of existing facilities needed to attain service and educational objectives.

18. Participates in the planning and maintenance of quality preservice training programs for nursing personnel. Provides for orientation and inservice programs for all nursing personnel.

19. Develops agreements with educational agencies for the use of clinical facilities by nursing students.
   a. Determines the number of students that can be appropriately assigned to a clinical unit.
   b. Clarifies the responsibility of nursing service for the management of the patient's nursing care and the responsibility of nursing education for the student's learning experience.

20. Initiates, promotes, and participates when necessary in studies and research designed to assess nursing administrative practices and nursing care.

21. Promotes utilization of the applicable findings of studies and research for the improvement of nursing administrative practices and nursing care.

22. Collaborates in other suitable studies and research.
   a. Identifies the elements which may pose problems to the researcher, nursing personnel, and/or patients.
   b. Stipulates the standards of nursing care and practice which must be maintained for patients and personnel involved in research activities.

23. Participates in activities which promote his/her own professional growth and development.

24. Participates and promotes membership interest and participation in the activities of the professional nursing association, in allied health organizations, and supportive community activities.

The role of the *head nurse* is primarily to assure good patient care. In planning for high-quality care for all the patients on her floor or wing the head nurse must keep her staff morale high through good human relations. Where there is freedom from tension, less friction and antagonism will exist.[8]

The head nurse works with the entire health team which includes the physician as leader. Other members are the patient, his family, the graduate nurse (both private duty and staff nurses), and the social worker, the nutritionist, the clergyman, the occupational and physical therapists, and other allied professional workers.[9] Within the nursing unit under the head nurse are usually licensed professional and practical staff nurses and nursing aides.

The head nurse is responsible for the administration and management of the nursing service in a single clinical unit.[10] She assures the best possible care for all patients with full knowledge of the medical regimen for each. The degree to which she administers direct patient care or assigns this care to others depends on the size of the unit. She teaches patients self-care for optimum recovery and health. She cooperates with the medical staff, coordinates their activities relevant to patients, and sees that their orders are carried out. When one considers the fact that there is a different health team for every patient, it is evident that the head nurse has a complicated administrative job as she correlates the activities of her unit.

The head nurse maintains good interpersonal relations within her unit and between her staff and others on the health team, the patients, and their families. The head nurse teaches, evaluates, and counsels her staff as she supervises them. She orients new personnel and assists with staff education, giving on-the-spot, inservice training to untrained personnel. She keeps personnel informed of directives and policies, supervising the manner

[8] Doris Geitgey. *A Handbook for Head Nurses.* Philadelphia: F. A. Davis Co., 1962, p. 77.

[9] Eleanor C. Lambertsen. *Education for Nursing Leadership.* Philadelphia: J. B. Lippincott Co., 1958, p. 78.

[10] Mary Helen Barabas. *Contemporary Head Nursing.* New York: The Macmillan Co., 1962, p. 15.

in which these are carried out. She assigns responsibilities and working hours. This involves planning schedules two or three weeks in advance and making emergency adjustments when personnel are unable to report for work because of illness or weather conditions. Good planning provides for smooth operation of a unit.[11]

In summary, a head nurse participates in all the executive duties outlined by Gulick and Urwick with their hieroglyphic POSDCORB: Planning, Organizing, Staffing, Directing, Coordinating, Reporting, and Budgeting.[12]

Historically, the head nurse has been responsible for such activities as hostess, clerk, coordinator, and manager of the unit; administrator and coordinator of patient care; supervisor and teacher of nursing service staff.[13] Whereas the professional nurse should assume all responsibility in the area of patient care and staff development, there are other activities that are not actually nursing that can be handled by a well-trained unit manager.

A *unit manager* is now being used in many contemporary hospitals. This assignment needs an intelligent, well-trained person who can be a peer of the head nurse and not responsible to her; one who has a good sense of timing who is able to differentiate the essential from the nonessential.

The unit manager is responsible for nonnursing functions and should always be present at the central desk to greet or assist people who visit the unit, answer questions, direct friends and relatives to patients, greet doctors, and find the head nurse if additional information is needed. She directs the traffic flow of special therapists.

The object of the unit manager is to relieve the head nurse of all nonnursing functions in order to free her to perform more

[11] Tiny M. Calander. *Unit Administration*. Philadelphia: W. B. Saunders Co., 1962, p. 20.

[12] Luther Gulick and L. Urwick (eds.). *Papers on the Science of Administration*. New York: Institute of Public Administration, 1937.

[13] Barrett, Jean. *The Head Nurse*. New York: Appleton-Century-Crofts, 1962, p. 38.

tasks for which she has been educated. To achieve this management goal it is necessary to procure and maintain all the equipment and supplies needed by nurses. It is also essential to make sure rooms are ready for new patients and that clothes and valuables are taken care of in accordance with hospital policy. With the assistance of nonnursing personnel the unit manager cares for used equipment such as treatment trays and waste materials according to hospital procedure. The unit manager is responsible for supplies, the provision of linen and other necessities such as thermometers, and bedside equipment including the collection, washing, and refilling of water pitchers.[14]

Not many hospitals have a unit helper assigned to the patient division but recognition of this type of service is rapidly developing.

WHO ELSE IS INVOLVED IN PATIENT-CENTERED CARE?

In addition to the medical and nursing staff the patient is in contact with people from the many other professional and institutional services.

Professional services include:

1. *Pathology and the Laboratory.* The laboratory is directed by a doctor who has specialized in pathology. His staff are medical technologists who perform such procedures as blood counts, blood sugars, urinalyses, and tissue analyses. The laboratory is usually responsible for the blood bank except in very large institutions.

2. *Radiology.* The director of the x-ray department is a doctor who has specialized in radiology. The department is staffed with technicians who x-ray patients, develop films, and assist with diagnostic procedures such as fluoroscopy and x-ray examinations of digestive and urinary systems.

[14] *Ibid.,* p. 41.

3. *Pharmacy.* The pharmacy has at least one registered pharmacist who fills the doctors' prescriptions, which are sent to the wards and administered by registered nurses.

4. *Social Service.* This department is staffed by accredited social workers, one of whom serves as director. The social service acts as liaison between the home and the hospital, counseling the patient and his family with both family relations and economic problems.

5. *Medical Dietary.* This facility is staffed by a dietitian who directs the preparation of food for patients on medical diets prescribed by the physician.

6. *Speech Pathology and Audiology.* This area of professional specialization has developed out of concern for people with speech, language, and hearing disorders. Speech clinicians provide clinical services to assist children and adults in overcoming handicaps incurred by speech, language, and hearing problems.

7. *Physical Therapy.* The physical therapist is a professional health worker who, upon the referral of a physician:
Evaluates the patient by performing specific tests to determine neurologic, musculoskeletal, respiratory, and cardiovascular status;
Plans a treatment program for the patient as a result of the evaluation;
Utilizes physical measures and instructs the patient as part of the over-all treatment program for the patient;
Applies appropriate psychologic and sociologic principles in determining and carrying out the treatment program;
Instructs nonprofessional workers, members of the patient's family, and family substitutes in carrying out specific procedures and supervises their activity;
Communicates and cooperates effectively with other health workers in the total rehabilitation effort;

Functions in the prevention of disabilities, particularly of the musculoskeletal system.[15]

8. *Occupational Therapy.* Occupational therapy is the use of purposeful activity as treatment in the rehabilitation of persons with physical or emotional disability. The occupational therapist, as a vital member of the rehabilitation team, works in consultation with qualified physicians, physical and speech therapists, nurses, social workers, psychologists, vocational counselors, teachers, and other specialists. The objectives of the treatment program are determined by the occupational therapist according to the individual needs of each patient and may include:

Decreasing or eliminating disability during the patient's initial phases of recovery following injury or illness;

Increasing or maintaining the individual's capability for independence and his physical, emotional, and social well-being;

Developing total function to a maximum level through early evaluation and experimentation for future job training and employment.

By individual or group participation in supervised activity, the patient is helped to solve some of his problems and to increase his usefulness.[16]

9. *Central Sterile Supply.* This department is responsible for providing supplies and equipment required by all departments that render patient care, at the time needed, of the right quality and quantity, and in the proper condition for use. The objectives of the department are to provide:

Supplies and equipment from a central department where all processing of such supplies and equipment is conducted

[15] Mary Elizabeth Kolb. "The Challenge of Success," *Physical Therapy*, **46:** 1159, 1966.

[16] American Occupational Therapy Association. *Occupational Therapy Handbook.* New York: American Occupational Therapy Ass., 1965.

under controlled conditions, thereby contributing to total
environmental control in the hospital;

Greater economy by centralizing expensive processing
equipment in one central area;

More uniformity by standardizing supplies, equipment, and
techniques of operation; and

More efficiency by training workers in precise processing
procedures.[17]

All department heads are responsible to the hospital administrator and require some established form of organization. By
working together, all these people strive for unity of purpose in
spite of the fact that each department is engrossed in its own
area of specialization. Each department has its own channel of
authority.

Since every department has specific functions peculiar to its
specialty, it naturally follows that the administrative responsibility would vary greatly.

Each specialty has supportive personnel, assistants, or aides,
who help with transportation, record keeping, and such time-
consuming jobs as assisting the patient to dress and undress and
preparing treatment areas for the therapist, clerical, and messen-
ger service.

All the functions of administration described later in this book
apply to the responsibilities of the heads of the departments and
the chiefs of the various specialties.

Esther Lucile Brown cites a case called "Hospital Hierarchy"
which discusses how hospital personnel can be recognized and
placed within the hierarchy by what they wear. The doctor, for
instance, wears a clean, white, full-length coat, while the laboratory personnel wear white coats that are often full of acid holes.
The nurses wear white and identifying caps, and the aides wear

[17] Public Health Service, U.S. Department of Health, Education, and
Welfare. *Administrative Aspects of Hospital Central Medical and Surgical
Supply Services.* Washington, D.C.: U.S. Government Printing Office, 1966,
p. 1.

pink, while the poor patient falls at the very bottom of the hierarchy, dressed, alas, in a short white shirt that does not even cover him and is open down the back.[18] Stripped of his authority as well as his clothes, the patient finds out very quickly that he is absolutely low man on the totem pole. He must obey the orders of everyone, from the aide who comes to transport him to some other department for testing and treatment to the doctor whose authoritative word is needed before any "privileges" may be granted. Quite the opposite, the patient should be made to feel that he is *the* person around whom the whole hospital functions. Its purpose is to be of service to him. All patients find themselves uprooted from their daily ways of life during their hospital stay, and their disorientation is compounded by their illness, pain, and discomfort. Administrative planning must try to maintain some continuity with the patient's accustomed pattern of living.

It is the role of all department heads to keep uppermost as their purpose the welfare of patients who are temporarily their responsibility. Conscientiousness within the department is a desirable quality. Such sensitivity can only be reflected through the hospital administrator, the board, and, in turn, through department heads to all workers.[19]

No medical specialty can abrogate to itself the full responsibility for administration of the total spectrum of comprehensive patient-centered care, nor can other professional disciplines assume or perform this responsibility. Prominent in the medical language today is the word "teamwork." Teamwork involves a three-dimensional approach: intradepartmental, with the physician as the leader or supervisor; interdepartmental within the individual therapeutic units; and interagency, private or public. In order for these departments to coordinate their activities, leader-

[18] Esther Lucile Brown. *Newer Dimensions in Patient Care,* Part 2. New York: Russell Sage Foundation, 1961, p. 165.

[19] Herman Finer. *Administration and the Nursing Service.* New York: The Macmillan Co., 1952, p. 222.

ship must be assumed by every department head, who accepts the leadership of the medical staff and hospital administrator.

Institutional services are organized in various ways depending on the size and purpose of the hospital.

1. There is usually an assistant administrator in charge of financing to include accounting, credit, payroll, and purchasing.

2. Hospitals need an engineer in charge of maintenance. Under his direction are electricians, plumbers, carpenters, painters, mechanics, and other people who are caring for buildings and grounds.

3. There is the housekeeping department in charge of a specially trained person directing the activities of those who keep the "house" clean.

4. There are many other people who direct the activities of medical records, admissions, personnel, library, medical secretaries, and volunteer workers.

Without institutional services, the patient could not be cared for and the professional services could not function. All institutional services administrators are responsible to the hospital administrator. Although the hospital administrator is not deeply involved with the daily activities of these units, he is ultimately responsible for seeing that the institution is well serviced. The hospital administrator becomes immediately involved in such instances as labor union problems or situations where legal complications could or do develop.

HOW DID ADMINISTRATION DEVELOP IN HOSPITALS?

Medical institutions for the care and shelter of the sick first appeared in Rome. Guiding motives for their development were for military or economic purposes related to the structure and purposes of the Roman society. The concept of a need for social assistance in case of illness was highly developed during the Middle Ages, particularly among the Moslems, Jews, and Christians.[20]

According to Faxon, hospitals have belonged to the social order, fulfilling the needs of society in ways that society could provide. When medical science was primitive, the doctor neither required nor controlled many facilities. With Lister's discovery of the principles of antisepsis and asepsis the medical profession embarked on a great expansion of surgery and all classes of society sought knowledge and skill rather than faith and miracles. More patients needed hospital care. This placed more responsibility squarely on the hospital, for the doctors found the hospital essential for proper care of major illness. This blending of the doctor's interest and the function of the hospital led to a sense of responsibility and ownership. The institution was no longer thought of as an agency of society by the doctor. A professional medical hierarchy developed which had no relation to the ownership of the hospital. Practitioners in control of wards held their positions by virtue of long and well-performed services that brought advancement by rigid rules of seniority.[21]

As knowledge and technical facilities grew, there was an increase in the number of medical and technical personnel required by the hospital. In some hospitals, as these changes occurred, the medical chief-of-staff had a great deal of responsibility. As administrative problems increased, the need for special training in hospital administration and in business was apparent, and schools of hospital administration were established. The first of these was in Chicago in 1933. Others developed as doctors were called into the service for World War II.

[20] Eliot Freidson. *The Hospital in Modern Society.* New York: The Free Press of Glencoe, 1963, p. 2.

[21] Nathaniel W. Faxon. *The Hospital in Contemporary Life.* Cambridge: Harvard University Press, 1949, p. 61.

SUMMARY

A hospital consists of a building or group of buildings, space, equipment, skilled people, and patients. A hospital may be classified as voluntary, government, or proprietary. Hospitals provide medical and institutional services for patient-centered care. Chapter 2 discussed these services in detail and defined the functions of the director of nursing services, the head nurse, her staff, and other professional services including pathology, radiology, pharmacy, social service, medical dietary, physical therapy, occupational therapy, speech therapy, and central sterile supply.

The organization of institutional services was discussed, and a brief presentation concerning how administration developed was included.

Bibliography

American Hospital Association and National League of Nursing Education. *Hospital Nursing Service Manual.* New York: National League of Nursing Education, 1950.

American Nurses' Association. *Statement of Functions and Qualifications for Nursing Service Administrators.* New York: American Nurses' Association, August, 1966, p. 2.

American Occupational Therapy Association. *Occupational Therapy Handbook.* New York: American Occupational Therapy Association, 1965.

Barabas, Mary Helen. *Contemporary Head Nursing.* New York: The Macmillan Co., 1962.

Barrett, Jean. *The Head Nurse.* New York: Appleton-Century-Crofts, 1962, pp. 38, 41.

Brown, Esther Lucile. *Newer Dimensions in Patient Care*, Part 2. New York: Russell Sage Foundation, 1961.

Calander, Tiny M. *Unit Administration.* Philadelphia: W. B. Saunders Co., 1962.

Department of Hospital Nursing, National League for Nursing. *The Head Nurse at Work*. New York: National League for Nursing, 1953.

Faxon, Nathaniel W. *The Hospital in Contemporary Life*. Cambridge: Harvard University Press, 1949.

Finer, Herman. *Administration and the Nursing Service*. New York: The Macmillan Co., 1952.

Freidson, Eliot. *The Hospital in Modern Society*. New York: The Free Press of Glencoe, 1963.

Gallagher, Anna Helen. *Educational Administration in Nursing*. New York: The Macmillan Co., 1965.

Geitgey, Doris. *A Handbook for Head Nurses*. Philadelphia: F. A. Davis Co., 1962.

Gulick, Luther, and L. Urwick (eds.). *Papers on the Science of Administration*. New York: Institute of Public Administration, 1937.

Kolb, Mary Elizabeth. "The Challenge of Success," *Physical Therapy*, **46:** 1159, 1966.

Lambertsen, Eleanor C. *Education for Nursing Leadership*. Philadelphia: J. B. Lippincott Co., 1958.

Public Health Service, U.S. Department of Health, Education, and Welfare. *Administrative Aspects of Hospital Central Medical and Surgical Supply Services*. Washington, D.C.: U.S. Government Printing Office, 1966, p. 1.

Sloan, Raymond P. *This Hospital Business of Ours*. New York: G. P. Putnam's Sons, 1952.

———. *Today's Hospital*. New York: Harper and Row, 1966.

Chapter 4

The Administration of the Hospital

WHO IS LEGALLY RESPONSIBLE FOR THE OPERATION OF THE HOSPITAL?

The board of directors is legally responsible for the operation of the hospital. Sloan describes the responsibilities of the board in the following six categories: [1]

(1) Purpose (this involves the extent of patient care, education and research); (2) financial; (3) facilities and personnel; (4) professional; (5) public relations; and (6) quality of medical care.

He further states that the "board is responsible to the patient, to the community and to the sponsoring organization. Thus, the trustee represents a corporation that is liable for negligent treatment on the part of physicians he appoints." [2]

WHAT ARE THE FUNCTIONS OF THE BOARD?

The function of the board is to assume legal responsibility for operation of the hospital and approve all policies. There is a fur-

[1] Raymond P. Sloan. *Today's Hospital.* New York: Harper and Row, 1966, p. 56.
[2] *Ibid.,* p. 57.

ther responsibility to defend the administration or any of those who work in the institution from improper pressure. Mere defense is not enough. It is up to the board to handle problems that arise from constituency pressures and also to interpret the institution to the public. The board appoints the hospital administrator. In many areas the administrator acts as a member ex officio of the board of trustees.

HOW DOES THE BOARD OPERATE?

The ways in which the board carries out its responsibilities have been described in the 1964 revision of the Code of Ethics developed jointly by the American Hospital Association and the American College of Hospital Administrators.[3] It states the following basic principles of organization:

> The legally constituted governing body is the supreme authority of the hospital and should have full responsibility for its conduct and efficient administration.
>
> The members of the governing body are obligated to uphold the high office of community trust which has been placed in them. They must conscientiously fulfill all statutory requirements and scrupulously perform all duties prescribed by the corporate constitution and bylaws. In discharging its responsibilities, the governing body, at all times, must be impartial, fair and objective.
>
> The governing body of the hospital should recognize that with the medical staff it forms what is essentially a cooperative relationship supported by the community to perform the recognized functions of a hospital.
>
> To assure the patient every reasonable protection,

[3] American Hospital Association and American College of Hospital Administrators. *Code of Ethics.* Chicago: American Hospital Association, 1964, p. 2.

thereby fulfilling its moral and legal responsibility, the following administrative principles are recommended for the governing body:

a) To adopt suitable bylaws and to establish a plan of organization providing single and distinct lines of authority and responsibility;

b) To select a competent administrator;

c) To determine the policies of the institution with regard to relations to community needs and internal organization and operation. The governing body's activities should be essentially those concerned with the policy formation rather than administrative procedure;

d) To provide equipment and facilities commensurate with the needs of patients admitted to the hospital;

e) To select a competent and qualified medical staff;

f) To provide methods by which the organized medical staff advises the administrator and the governing body on professional matters;

g) To maintain recognized professional standards in the care of the sick, and to ensure that the financial interests of the hospital should never be a cause for any deviation from a high standard of competence and procedure on the part of physicians, nurses or others appointed to work in the hospital;

h) To coordinate professional interests with administrative, financial and community needs;

i) To enforce businesslike management of the financial affairs of the hospital; to provide for a safe administration of funds given in trust; to keep accurate records of finances and activities, including an annual audit, and to provide adequate financing by securing sufficient income;

j) To establish and maintain sound personnel policies in the hospital;

k) To ensure that no member of the governing body, or

any other person, uses his affiliation with the hospital for personal, financial or material gain;

1) To be alert and responsive to the changing needs of the community for hospital resources.

WHO IS THE HOSPITAL ADMINISTRATOR?

As everybody knows, an executive has practically nothing to do. That is EXCEPT to decide what is to be done; to tell somebody to do it; to listen to reasons why it should be done a different way. EXCEPT to follow up to see if the thing has been done; to discover that it has not been done; to listen to excuses from the person who should have done it and did not do it. EXCEPT to follow up a second time to see if the thing has been done; to discover that it has been done, but done incorrectly; to point how it should have been done; to wonder if it is not time to get rid of a person who cannot do a thing correctly; to reflect that the person in fault has a wife and seven children. EXCEPT to consider how much simpler and better the thing would have been done had he done it himself in the first place, but to realize that such an idea would strike at the very foundation of the belief of all employees that an executive has nothing to do! [4]

The hospital administrator is the person appointed by the board to integrate and coordinate the business of the hospital. The administrator acts in an over-all executive capacity. He is directly responsible for the conduct of all internal affairs.

Hospital administrators have various titles according to the policy of the hospital. They sometimes have the title of president or vice-president. They may also be called executive director and

[4] *The Covington News,* Andalusia, Alabama, Dec. 18, 1947. Quoted in Albert Lepawsky, *Administration: The Art and Science of Organization and Management.* New York: Alfred A. Knopf, 1960, p. 323.

their assistants may have the title of associate executive director.

WHY IS IT NECESSARY TO HAVE A HOSPITAL ADMINISTRATOR?

Every hospital needs an administrator to serve in a pivotal position.

1. The legally responsible group in the hospital, charged with legislative policy, is the board of trustees; therefore they must be the policy makers.
2. The essential activity in the hospital is medical care for the sick, a specialty of physicians; therefore they should determine the policies of the organization.
3. The person most knowledgeable about all phases of life in the hospital, the only full-time professional with wide perspective is the administrator; therefore he should decide policy.[5]

The above quote illustrates how complicated the administrator's role can be. Every organization needs a central coordinator to work with all facets and to assure that things are running as smoothly as possible.

The hospital administrator is directly responsible to the board. Although he may serve as pivot man between the board and the medical staff through the joint conference committee, it is the board who hires him and delegates to him full responsibility to administer the total business of the hospital.

WHAT DOES A HOSPITAL ADMINISTRATOR DO?

It is the responsibility of the hospital administrator to make each department realize it exists *to get something done.* He

[5] Arthur B. Moss, Wayne G. Broehl, Jr., Robert H. Guest, and John W. Hennessey, Jr. *Hospital Policy Decisions.* New York: G. P. Putnam's Sons, 1966, p. 86.

knows that no agency will go ahead by itself no matter how well it is organized. He must sort the primary from the secondary aims. He is aware of the express needs and the desires of the group with whom he works. To accomplish the goals of the hospital he:

1. Establishes Sound Organization

To fulfill major responsibilities satisfactorily the hospital administrator must establish sound organization. He must make certain that all the assistant administrators and department heads are accountable to him in a clearly defined and well-understood way. It is his responsibility to see that these people are the best available persons for their positions. He must limit to a manageable scope the number of persons who report to him. To these people he delegates authority to carry out specific functions. Then he must follow up these delegations to assure himself that the objectives and policies of the board of trustees are being carried out.

2. Holds Leaders Together

Once the hospital administrator makes certain that the day-to-day affairs will be capably handled, he is free for more important matters, such as working with the board and its committees or with the medical and nursing staff. The well-educated hospital administrator will know how to develop techniques and methods which tie the leaders of the hospital staff into a working group.[6]

A hospital administrator willingly accepts assistance from any member of the staff. The man or woman who is a hospital administrator must be personally respected by the hospital personnel and by the people of the community the hospital serves. He must also be a person of integrity and good character.

The chief executive of any large hospital today is seldom an individual entrepreneur who began his career as the guiding en-

[6] Harlow J. Heneman. "Administrators Waste Time Chasing Details," *The Modern Hospital,* 99: 87, 1962.

gineer or medical genius behind his establishment. He is much more likely to be a professionally trained manager, attempting to arbitrate among the conflicting interests of a series of specialized departments. These are run by other professionals who are in a position to challenge his decisions.[7]

3. Coordinates Activities

As one of his major functions, the hospital administrator assumes a leadership role with the members of the board. In addition to this he must see that the internal administration of the hospital operates effectively and efficiently. He carries out the policies and objectives approved by the board. It is his responsibility to see that the medical staff functions as a constructive, positive element in management. By coordinating the activities of the medical staff with those of other departments he provides administrative support for the medical staff and the departments of the hospital.

4. Makes Decisions

The hospital administrator makes decisions that specify the functions of those working within the various departments. He outlines the general scope and nature of their duties. The administrator delegates authority, deciding who in the organization is to have power to make further decisions.

Normal human relationships do not spontaneously result in harmonious or productive outcomes. The wise administrator will plan carefully for successful situations considering both personal adjustments and group relations. He will then be concerned about every individual in his organization and see that each is given an opportunity for expression of his ideas.

5. Reviews Existing Policies

It is the administrator's responsibility to review existing policies, evaluate them, and, when necessary, initiate action of the board of directors to establish new policies.

[7] Joseph K. Owen (ed.). *Modern Concepts of Hospital Administration.* Philadelphia: W. B. Saunders Co., 1962, p. 759.

6. Lays Foundations

It is the distinct privilege of today's hospital administrator to lay foundations for the increased usefulness of the hospital in the future. This can only be done by observing trends in clinical medical care and being aware of the changing attitudes in medical economics and patterns of developing social and health legislation. An alert administrator will suggest to the board and the medical staff any possible developments in service and redirection of clinical or educational emphasis. Since the board is constantly changing, the progressive administrator must strive to lead his hospital toward greater effectiveness.

7. Plans, Persuades, and Manages

A good administrator will first *plan* carefully what he is going to do in order to obtain the ultimate goals of the organization. Following this he will *persuade* others working with him to want to obtain the same goals and work toward them. Finally, it is a task of *managing* to assure successful completion of the job to be done. This is a continuing and ongoing process.

8. Delegates Work

Every employee of a medical institution assumes, to some degree, a share of the work of administration. Even when following orders, personnel must assume some responsibility in carrying them out. This often involves giving further orders to someone else. It is important that all workers have some knowledge of administration.

Employees going to work in a medical center for the first time are often confused by the number of people giving them orders and directions. Although many centers provide booklets to orient employees, lack of time often prevents adequate orientation to the institution. The hospital administrator is conventionally thought of as the only administrator in the hospital. However, in the medical environment people in every department have many administrative functions. Employees with little or no administrative function should find out to whom they are directly responsible. Usually they will be told to whom they are directly responsible, and from this person they can learn which of the administrators they will be working with and what they do.

WHAT IS THE MEDICAL STAFF OF THE HOSPITAL?

The doctor using the hospital facilities becomes a member of the active medical staff. There are usually two officers, the president of the staff and the chief-of-staff. The president is the administrative officer of the medical staff while the chief-of-staff is the professional or clinical head. There is no absolute rule about this, but a large percentage of the medical staffs are organized in this fashion.

Armed forces hospitals, university hospitals, and government hospitals usually have paid medical directors. Other hospitals usually elect by majority vote their president and chief-of-staff and the board approves these appointments.[8] An effective, acceptable chief-of-staff could serve for several years in order to develop a continuing program.

HOW DOES THE MEDICAL STAFF FUNCTION?

The medical staff functions through its committee structure. There is usually an executive committee which is representative of the entire medical staff and responsible to it and the governing board. The functions and responsibilities of the executive committee are as follows: [9]

1. To coordinate the activities and general policies of the medical staff and departments of the staff.
2. To act for the staff as a whole under such limitations as may be imposed by the medical staff and its bylaws, rules and regulations.

[8] American Hospital Association. *Hospital Accreditation References.* Chicago: American Hospital Association, 1964, p. 62.
[9] *Ibid.,* p. 63.

3. To receive and act upon the reports of the medical records, tissue and credentials committees, and such other committees as the medical staff may designate.
4. To carefully consider and recommend action to the administrator on all matters which are of a medical-administrative nature.
5. To investigate any breach of ethics by members of the medical staff, as referred to this committee by the credentials committee.
6. To act as the program committee for staff meetings, unless this responsibility is delegated to a specific committee.

The medical staff also has a medical records committee composed of a representative cross-section of the clinical services provided by the hospital. This committee's work is often done for the most part by the medical records librarian, under the direction of the committee.

There is a tissue committee, whose main function is to improve surgical care of patients by review of documented work. Thus, this committee's work is one of continuing education with the pathologist as a member ex officio.

There is a credentials committee, which recommends new staff members to the board for appointment.

The committees discussed here are merely examples of the most prominent ones.

The medical staff also functions through meetings of the staff and departmental meetings which are held for the purpose of reviewing the medical care of patients within the hospital and those recently discharged.

In addition, the medical staff has a joint conference committee for liaison between the board and the medical staff. Its purposes are as follows: [10]

> Its purposes, all directed toward better patient care, should be at least three:

[10] *Ibid.*, p. 66.

a. Communications, to keep board, staff, and administration cognizant of pertinent actions taken or contemplated by one or the other. These should be reported to the committee even though they do not require action by more than one component of it. Open communications through the joint conference committee will emphasize the importance of prior knowledge of all affected groups before action is instituted and will thus prevent misunderstanding.

b. Planning. Plans for growth and inevitable change in the hospital organization should be considered by this committee.

c. Problems. Issues which arise in the operation and affairs of the hospital affecting all parties should be brought to the committee for consideration.

WHAT ARE THE RELATIONSHIPS BETWEEN THE MEDICAL STAFF AND THE TRUSTEES, THE HOSPITAL ADMINISTRATOR, AND MEDICAL AS WELL AS INSTITUTIONAL SERVICES?

Through committee functions the medical staff has contact with the board as well as the hospital administrator. They have a voice in every aspect of patient care and are responsible for their patients who receive care in the hospital. Therefore, the scope of their influence pervades the entire institution as they work with individual patients or function as a member of the medical staff or one of its committees.

SUMMARY

The board of directors is legally responsible for the operation of the hospital. It is responsible to the patient, to the community, and to the sponsoring organization. The board appoints the hospital administrator, who coordinates the business of the hospital. He is directly responsible for the conduct of all internal affairs. The hospital administrator:

1. Establishes sound organization
2. Holds leaders together
3. Coordinates activities
4. Makes decisions
5. Reviews existing policies
6. Lays foundations
7. Plans, persuades, and manages
8. Delegates work

The medical staff is composed of the doctors using the hospital facilities. It functions through a committee structure and through meetings of the staff to review the medical care of patients within the hospital. Through committee functions the medical staff has contact with the board as well as the hospital administrator.

Chapter 5 deals with hospital policies and why they are necessary.

Bibliography

American Hospital Association. *Hospital Accreditation References*. Chicago: American Hospital Association, 1964.

American Hospital Association and American College of Hospital Administrators. *Code of Ethics*. Chicago: American Hospital Association, 1964.

The Covington News, Andalusia, Alabama, Dec. 18, 1947. Quoted in Albert Lepawsky, *Administration: The Art and Science of Organization and Management*. New York: Alfred A. Knopf, 1960.

Heneman, Harlow J. "Administrators Waste Time Chasing Details," *The Modern Hospital,* 99: 87, 1962.

Moss, Arthur B., Wayne G. Broehl, Jr., Robert H. Guest, and

John W. Hennessey, Jr. *Hospital Policy Decisions.* New York: G. P. Putnam's Sons, 1966.

Owen, Joseph K. (ed.). *Modern Concepts of Hospital Administration.* Philadelphia: W. B. Saunders Co., 1962.

Sloan, Raymond P. *Today's Hospital.* New York: Harper and Row, 1966.

Operational Procedures

WHAT ARE POLICIES?

Hospitals have different types of policies at all levels. There are many kinds of policies, including "over-all" hospital policies such as the number of hours personnel will work, policies concerning a basis for hiring and firing, policies concerning the operating-room schedule, and policies concerning fringe benefits. There are policies about standards of patient care and policies about function of personnel. Policies are guides for action. Procedures are means by which the policies are implemented. Many procedures may vary according to the situation.

Policies are defined as "settled courses adopted and followed." [1]

Policies include both institutional objectives and the plans to achieve them—through determination, review, and modification. All policies are subject to change owing to the development of new conditions and new procedures. The more important and controlling policy making is the responsibility of the governing board.

The elements of institutional policies include (1) the objective sought, (2) the delegated responsibility for devising plans and

[1] John D. Millett. *The Academic Community*. New York: McGraw-Hill Book Co., Inc., 1962, p. 64.

supervising operations necessary to achieve the purposes, (3) the organization required to achieve the purposes, and (4) the methods and procedures appropriate to realization of the objectives sought.[2]

The execution of policies of an organization is often difficult to administrate owing to the fact that employees are not aware of them. New employees find out what policies affect them directly through their administrator. Ideally they would be given enough orientation to know the total institutional policies, but this is seldom possible owing to the pressure of immediate tasks which need to be done.

The policy process centers on continuing activities directed to a choice of organizational goals and the means of achievement. The primary responsibility of the hospital is to render care to the sick and injured. All policies and procedures will reflect the thought that it is a privilege and responsibility to care for the sick with respect and compassion. The patient is a guest, the most important person in the hospital. The safety of patients is therefore one of the hospital's most important policies.[3]

Relationships with the board of trustees, the doctors, nurses, and other professionals are often defined in policy statements which explain how their mutual goals will be attained.

WHY ARE POLICIES NECESSARY?

Policies are necessary in order to provide uniform communication throughout all departments. Through well-established and pertinent policies employees are in a better position to know what is expected of them. Policies are useful aids to supervisors and department heads who interpret them for employees. In

2 Thad L. Hungate. *Management in Higher Education.* New York: Bureau of Publication, Teachers College, Columbia University, 1964, p. 69.

3 Arthur B. Moss, Wayne G. Broehl, Jr., Robert H. Guest, and John W. Hennessey, Jr. *Hospital Policy Decisions.* New York: G. P. Putnam's Sons, 1966, p. 3.

order to do this the supervisors and department heads need to be familiar with hospital policies.

An institution in which employees not only know what is expected of them, but why it is expected, has taken the first step toward attaining better patient care through a better adjusted, better informed, happier work force.[4]

WHAT ARE PERSONNEL POLICIES?

The process of administrating hospitals revolves around operational policies which are either general or specific in nature. A general policy would state that all personnel would be granted paid vacations after one year of service. A specific policy would state that all *clerical* personnel would receive two weeks' paid vacation after one year of service. Owen suggests the following general headings for personnel policies: [5]

1. A statement of cooperation—joint interest of hospital and employee and goals of each. The philosophy of the hospital with regard to relations with its employees.
2. Requirements of employment.
3. Conditions of employment (hours, wages, holidays, vacations, absences, etc.).
4. Promotion and transfer.
5. Disciplinary policies.
6. Grievance procedure.
7. Termination procedure (voluntary—involuntary).
8. Employee health program.
9. Employee benefits (insurance, retirement, hospitalization, educational assistance, etc.).

[4] Joseph Karlton Owen (ed.). *Modern Concepts of Hospital Administration.* Philadelphia: W. B. Saunders Co., 1961, p. 132.
[5] *Ibid.*

The hospital administrator, working with the board of directors and all other personnel, has a responsibility to conduct research into existing policies and practices. Operational policies need to be analyzed and evaluated as to effectiveness; then, if necessary, new ones should be developed.

SUMMARY

Hospitals have different policies at all levels. Policies are defined as settled courses adopted and followed and should include the thought that it is a privilege and responsibility to care for the sick with respect and compassion. Relationships with the board of trustees, the doctors, nurses, and other professionals are often defined as policy statements which explain how their mutual goals will be attained.

Policies are necessary in order to provide uniform communication throughout all departments. The process of administrating hospitals revolves around operational policies which are either general or specific in nature. Operational policies need to be analyzed and evaluated as to effectiveness; then, if necessary, new ones should be developed.

Bibliography

Hungate, Thad L. *Management in Higher Education.* New York: Bureau of Publications, Teachers College, Columbia University, 1964.

Millett, John D. *The Academic Community.* New York: McGraw-Hill Book Co., Inc., 1962.

Moss, Arthur B., Wayne G. Broehl, Jr., Robert H. Guest, and John W. Hennessey, Jr. *Hospital Policy Decisions.* New York: G. P. Putnam's Sons, 1966.

Owen, Joseph Karlton (ed.). *Modern Concepts of Hospital Administration.* Philadelphia: W. B. Saunders Co., 1961.

Chapter 6

Ethical and Legal Influences

All persons in administrative positions are responsible for the ethical and legal behavior of those who work under their guidance. Interpretation of ethical and legal controls and influences can become very complicated, especially for the student or employee new to the medical environment. The following discussion will serve as a guide for those making ethical and legal decisions and for understanding the necessary decisions made by administrators.

Ever since the Hippocratic oath was formulated (400 B.C.) medical codes of ethics have consistently followed the pattern set at that ancient time. They have become an integral part of the *modus operandi* in hospitals and medical institutions. Although the wording is ancient, the ethical concern for the welfare of the patient is obvious.

THE HIPPOCRATIC OATH

I swear, by Apollo the physician, and Ausculapius, and Health, and Allheal, and all the gods and goddesses, that, according to my ability and judgment, I will keep this Oath and this stipulation—to reckon him who taught me this Art equally dear to me as my parents, to share my substance with him, and relieve his necessities if required; to look upon his offspring in the same footing as my own brothers, and to teach them this art, if they shall wish to learn it, without fee or stipulation; and that by precept, lecture, and every other mode of instruction, I will impart a knowledge of the Art to my own sons, and those of my teachers, and to disciples bound by a stipulation and oath according to the law of medicine, but to none others. I will follow that system of regimen which, according to my ability and judgment, I consider for the benefit of my patients, and abstain from whatever is deleterious and mischievous. I will give no deadly medicine to any one if asked nor suggest any such counsel; and in like manner I will not give a woman a pessary to produce abortion. With purity and with holiness I will pass my life and practice my Art. I will not cut persons laboring under the stone, but will leave this to be done by men who are practitioners of this work. Into whatever houses I enter, I will go into them for the benefit of the sick, and will abstain from every voluntary act of mischief and corruption; and further from the seduction of females or males, or freemen and slaves. Whatever, in connection with my professional practice or not, in connection with it, I see or hear in the life of men, which ought not to be spoken of abroad, I will not divulge, as reckoning that all such should be kept secret. While I continue to keep this Oath unviolated, may it be granted to me to enjoy life and the practice of the art, respected by all men, in all times! But should I trespass and violate this Oath, may the reverse be my lot!

WHY IS IT NECESSARY TO KNOW ABOUT CODES OF ETHICS?

The word "ethics" comes from the Greek word *ethos*, meaning of or related to moral action. Ethics is the scientific and philosophic study of human conduct. Ethical responsibilities are established on a philosophic and practical basis to direct human behavior.[1] A keyword of ethics is "right." An act is either right or wrong. Therefore ethics is the study of right and wrong; of good and bad.[2] Ethics deals with human perfection. Human perfection can only be understood as the individual regards himself. If he acts honestly according to his own conscience, the act is morally good; however, when he acts against his conscience, that act is morally wrong. Therefore human perfection to an American would mean one thing and human perfection to an aborigine would mean a completely different thing, for people are strongly guided by ideas that seem ethically right to the society in which they live.

It takes strength of character to do that which the society you live in may not approve of or understand. In the motion picture *Cheaper by the Dozen,* Father Gilbreth insisted on chaperoning his daughter to the high school dance on her first date with the cheerleader. Of course, the daughter did not like this at all and she said, "Oh, Daddy! Do you have to do that? Nobody else's father will be there!" As long as Dr. Gilbreth thought it was right, he did it whether his daughter liked it or not and even though he was the only father at the dance.

WHY DO THE VARIOUS MEDICAL SPECIALTIES NEED CODES OF ETHICS?

These codes of ethics are meant to be practical. Ethical principles must be lived as well as thought and reasoned about. In a medical sense the word "ethics" refers to medical standards of moral behavior. Every branch of the medical field has its own code of ethics. All of these codes are designed to protect, eth-

[1] Dom Thomas Vernon Moore. *Principles of Ethics.* Philadelphia: J. B. Lippincott Co., 1943, pp. 3–8.

[2] T. V. Smith and William Debbins. *Constructive Ethics.* New York: Prentice-Hall, Inc., 1948, p. 1.

ically, legally, and morally, the patient, members of the medical professions, and the public. Basically the codes agree that the professional objectives are to give full measure of service and devotion to humanity. These codes state the need for professional people to strive to improve knowledge and proficiency in skills. They promise to safeguard the public and to disclose to the proper authorities any knowledge concerning unethical practice. They make it clear that there shall be no exploitation of the patient. They state that information of a confidential nature may not be revealed. They state that patients may not be solicited and specify the nature of the relationship between the various medical professions.

Every institution should have a philosophy and set of ethical standards. It should believe its goals are reasonably attainable and morally sound and will provide genuine satisfaction for all concerned. A clearly understood set of ethical standards will guide a human organization and provide a rallying point for all members. It was stated earlier that the first school for hospital administrators began in 1933. It is interesting to note that they had produced their own code of ethics by 1939, which was last revised in 1957.[3]

HOW CAN ETHICAL DECISIONS BE MADE?

Decisions that are morally right are not always easy to make. Often one may fear the loss of job and security from doing what one believes is morally right. Right action is that which is really reasonable and truly human. It is wrong if it is unreasonable and in some way less than human. In the work people have to do in hospitals it sometimes seems that what they are doing is less than human. For example, in working with a severely burned

[3] American College of Hospital Administrators and American Hospital Association. *Code of Ethics.* Chicago: American Hospital Association, 1957.

patient who is in great pain, it may be necessary *for his own good* to ask him to do something that causes more pain.

A common ethical error among medical workers is that they become concerned about their own reputation and demand perfection of a patient in order to further a good reputation for themselves. The result is that the patient is asked to work too hard. One should never go beyond the patient's endurance to satisfy his own professional ego. This could be done without the patient even being conscious of it, yet it would be morally wrong. Here again one's own human reason must be the guide. Experience and intelligent observation will help. Human reason is the best tool human beings have to arrive at solid ethical and moral decisions.

Another ethical hazard occurs when a patient states, "I have something to tell you, but I don't want you to tell anyone." The immediate answer ought to be, "Then don't tell me, because if I feel for any reason for your welfare it is better to tell someone, I will have to do so." Then if the patient continues, one is at least in the ethical position to relay necessary information to the doctor or other medical personnel interested in the welfare of the patient.

Learning to make ethical decisions requires reflection on one's own decisions and the decisions of others. The continual search for the objective truth will strengthen the chance that ethical decisions will be right. This sometimes means honest disagreement with the group. Development of strength of character is necessary; to simply always agree with the group means gradually collapsing into a "mush of concession." [4] True confidence in one's self develops only after one can recognize his own shortcomings as a person and as a member of the organization.

The opposite of that which is morally good is that which is morally evil. People tend to think in terms of that which is good and morally right as that which does not violate a law. One cannot pick up any book, code of ethics, bylaws, or even the Bible

[4] Richard Cabot. *The Meaning of Right and Wrong*. New York: The Macmillan Co., 1933, p. 173.

and, after reading it, say, "I will abide by this code and I will always be morally right." People associate that which is morally good with God, the truth, and state laws. It is still possible that any one of these might run contrary to what any one individual may consider morally right.

Since people are all brought up in different environments they all have somewhat different moral codes. It is difficult for people to know they will always be able to make decisions that are morally right. When dealing with the health of other people, one's conscience is often bothered by decisions. An example is the case of a patient with cancer who was very near death. She was in a great deal of pain and could not sleep at night. She begged a nurse to see if the doctor would give her some sleeping pills or something to relieve her pain. When the nurse talked to the doctor, he explained that the patient's condition was so precarious that a sleeping pill might cause her death. The nurse replied, "Well, so what! Certainly there is no hope for her life anyway." His reply was, "Are you asking me to commit murder?" The doctor had to make his own moral decision as to what was *right,* in this instance against the opinion of the nurse. He felt that anything that would hasten death was morally wrong. The nurse showed how she felt by replying, "In this case it seems to me morally wrong to let her suffer so."

The dividing line between that which is ethically right or wrong can often be very slim and often open to challenge. Ethics comes into play every time we are required to make a decision, whether this decision will affect other people or only ourselves. Before making decisions one must be sure he has all the facts. Quick decisions often have to be made. One cannot trust himself simply to follow the law and that which is legally right in order to know whether he is morally right or wrong. Too many legal loopholes can be used to commit moral errors. Ordinarily one's own conscience is the best guide. Even if these decisions mean loss of one's position, in no instance should a decision be made that could in any way harm the patient.

WHAT ARE SOME OF THE LEGAL CONTROLS NEEDED IN THE MEDICAL ENVIRONMENT?

Hospitals and their administrators need to be well aware of laws pertaining to licensure for their employees, contracts, negligence, malpractice, liability, and professional confidence. Administrators are also responsible for educating employees concerning the laws of the state that relate to medical care. Since the life and welfare of human beings is at stake (and since human beings are becoming more and more suit conscious) the necessity for abiding by the law and avoiding accidents or wrong decisions is important.

Dr. Helen Creighton, who is a lawyer and a nurse, has summarized those universal aspects of law of which medical professional people should be particularly aware. The material that follows is based on her articles which appeared in *The Physical Therapy Review*.[5]

Laws are written regulations concerning judicial decisions and statutes the purpose of which is to define the dividing line between each individual's freedom and his social responsibility. An individual's legal rights are those things which the law permits him to do, those freedoms it permits him to have. These rights are of two kinds: *primary*, or those rights inherent in the law, the possession of all members of society; and *secondary* rights, those rights which arise from a contract between two parties. Secondary rights do not extend beyond the parties involved. There are also third-party beneficiary contracts such as insurance policies. If an individual's primary or secondary rights are violated by someone else he has the right, called a *remedial* right, to obtain a proper remedy from the violator. The specific nature of the remedy either is written into the law or can be decided by

[5] Helen Creighton. "Law for Physical Therapists," *The Physical Therapy Review*, 38:22, 93, 165, 251, 1958.

a judge or jury. Some remedial rights often belong to the government; for instance, the state has the right to take action against violators of state traffic laws.

WHY ARE LICENSES NECESSARY?

One of the curbs on personal freedom for the protection of society is licensing. Because of the nature of the work in hospitals many of the duties may be done only by licensed personnel. The doctors, nurses, x-ray technicians, physical therapists, occupational therapists, speech therapists, and others must have licenses in order to work in their professions. Licenses are granted by the state government to those individuals who have proved their ability to perform the prescribed tasks by fulfilling the requirements set forth by the laws of the state. Licensing gives the state some legal control over persons performing these tasks. If someone without a medical license performs the duties of a doctor, for the payment of money, the state can take criminal action against him under a statute requiring a license. In this way there is some assurance that those practicing medicine or working at other vital jobs in medicine meet certain standards of competence and moral responsibility. That is, not only must they be skilled, but they must not use their skill to take advantage of the public.

Each state has its own laws regarding licenses, those who must be licensed, and what the requirements are. The student who is preparing for any medical job that might require a license should find out what the law is in his state. He would be wise, however, to fulfill the highest standards, so that he would be able to obtain a license and be employed in any state.

WHAT ARE CONTRACTS?

A contract is a promise or set of promises and may be verbal or in writing. Contracts are of importance to employees because it is by means of contracts that their working conditions are stipulated. Often these contracts are oral, and the employer and the employee depend on the good faith of one another to abide by the agreement. If a contract is to be legally binding, it must be written and signed by both parties. There need not be any witness to an oral contract for it to be binding. If an employer makes a written contract that he will hire someone for a year, but goes bankrupt before the end of that time, he can be held liable for the wages due in the remainder of the year to the extent provided by the Bankruptcy Act. Many states require that contracts that cannot be performed within a year from their date of execution must be in writing, signed by the party to be charged. In such a case an oral employment agreement by its terms to last for more than one year cannot be established by oral testimony.

A contract must contain the consent of both parties and both parties must be competent. A minor who has not been emancipated must have the consent of his parents since they are entitled to his services. As for the infant himself, he cannot be bound to a contract unless a court of competent jurisdiction has approved the same. A legally insane person would not be considered competent and would require consent of a guardian. A patient must be mentally competent when he signs permission for surgical procedures. (If a patient makes a verbal promise but dies before it is put in writing, one cannot legally consider this a contract and may not collect unless a disinterested third party can testify to the conversation.)

An employment contract should state the amount of the salary, the number of working hours, the amount of sick leave and vacation, and an indication of when a raise or promotion should be due. It must state what the responsibilities of the employees are, and it should indicate when notice for ending the contract, by either party, must be given.

Every contract must concern itself with a lawful object. For instance, one could not make a legal contract to sell narcotics. A contemporary misuse of the word "contact" is the underworld meaning, a contract to murder someone. This is not a lawful contract that would hold up in court. All parts of a contract must be within the law.

WHAT IS BREACH OF CONTRACT?

Breach of contract is a failure by a party to abide by any of the terms in a legally binding contract. The employer may refuse to pay as high a salary as he had agreed upon. The employee may not work as long as he had agreed to, or he may make continual errors in his work. There are times when the employee will break his contract without being aware of it. He may trade days off (legally called "substitution without permission") with someone and find later that his supervisor wanted him for something special that day. Failure to report to work without notifying the employer is considered breach of contract except in cases of death or "acts of God." An "act of God" is any catastrophe which could not be foreseen or avoided and which keeps the employee from getting to his job and from notifying his employer.

WHAT IS MALPRACTICE?

Malpractice usually involves those professions requiring a license: someone performing the duties of a licensed person without having a license, or a licensed person performing the duties incorrectly, inflicting harm on someone. Malpractice is broadly defined as "any professional misconduct, unreasonable lack of skill or fidelity in professional or judiciary duties, evil practice or illegal or immoral conduct." [6] The hospital employee must be careful not to overstep his responsibilities and he must be equally careful to perform correctly those duties which are his.

[6] Henry C. Black. *Black's Law Dictionary*. St. Paul: West Publishing Co., 1933.

It is usually the patient dissatisfied with the outcome of his treatment who will sue on a malpractice charge. The hospital employee must be careful in the handling of all patients since a pleasant atmosphere will help to keep the patient from developing any unwarranted antagonism. Louis J. Regan has listed these seven ways to help avoid malpractice suits: [7]

1. Be polite to patients regardless of circumstances.
2. Do not discuss the patients' ailments with them.
3. Do not discuss the respective merits of various forms of therapy.
4. Never prescribe.
5. Do not discuss other doctors with the patient.
6. Keep a record when the patient does not return as directed.
7. Be alert to hazards.

A survey taken in New York showed that one of the principal causes of malpractice claims is a failure to communicate. One example of such a misunderstanding follows: A doctor thought that the wrong boy had been brought to surgery; so he asked the boy, "Are you Fred?" The boy thought he said, "Are you afraid?" and he answered, "Yes." The wrong boy got the operation and the doctor got the lawsuit! [8]

Today this is not so likely to happen since now most hospitals use an identification bracelet. This bracelet is supposed to be checked by any employee giving treatment or transporting patients to surgery, x-ray or physical therapy, and so forth. Equally as important as verbal communication is the written record. For legal purposes all records should be kept in ink or typed so that they will not fade and cannot be erased. This applies to the patients' charts as well as to any records of financial charges and attendance.

[7] Louis J. Regan. *Doctor and Patient and the Law,* 3rd ed. St. Louis: C. V. Mosby Co., 1956.

[8] C. S. Blumel. "Ethics and Public Relations. The Physician's Responsibility to Patients and to Himself," *Rocky Mountain Medical Journal,* 58:32–36, 1961.

Another form of malpractice is the violation of professional confidence. Although a statement may be true, there is no defense in an action for breach of confidence. Any privileged information received about the patient by the doctor and given by the doctor to other employees is considered confidential. Any information offered by the patient is considered confidential. Such information cannot be discussed outside the professional group or for purposes other than the good of the patient. Libel is primarily a false statement which injures character or reputation or brings into ridicule. By statutes in many states the items may not be disclosed since these statutes create a legally protected right to privacy.

It is considered important to emphasize the difference between libel and slander. Libel is a defamatory statement made in writing to a third person unless the occasion for making it is privileged. If such a statement is made orally to a third person, it is slander and is often difficult to prove in court.

Professional people like laymen are answerable, bound, and obliged by law to fulfill their legal duties as prescribed by the law. If they do not, they are liable to those they injure. For example, if a professional person purchases equipment and does not pay for it within the prescribed time, he can be held liable for that debt.

WHAT IS NEGLIGENCE?

For all types of professional misconduct negligence and malpractice often overlap in meaning but the latter usually signifies willful wrongdoing, while negligence is unintentional. The hospital employee is more likely to be involved in a case of negligence. Negligence is carelessness which results in injury to a person or property. It is not difficult to imagine what kind of carelessness will result in injury: improper adjustment of equipment, forgetting a patient under a heat lamp, permitting a patient who is unable to try to walk alone. Under the law, negligence is relative: it is determined by deciding what a reasonable, prudent, responsible person would have done under the circumstances. However, the employee should consider himself always responsible and be constantly alert for accidents and errors even if he did not violate a legal obligation. He wants to protect himself and the hospital from any possible lawsuits, but more important he wants to protect the patient from any unnecessary injury.

In case of an accident, the employee should immediately make a written report, which should be filed in the event of a future suit by the patient. As there are some unscrupulous doctors who take advantage of the public, so are there unscrupulous patients, who, if they can, take advantage of the doctor and the hospital. For this reason careful records of accidents and unusual incidents can be helpful when it becomes necessary to reconstruct what actually happened. Lawyers in performing their obligation to their client may often use the records or their absence in a manner detrimental to hospital personnel.

Negligence can also involve the patient's property. When a patient enters the hospital his valuable articles should be placed in a safe for that purpose. Even outpatients should be warned to keep their possessions with them or to put them in a safe place. If patients are not given this chance to protect their belongings, the hospital can be held responsible for any loss. If a patient must undress, the nurse or aide in charge should see that his clothes and possessions are safe. The hospital should have a firm policy in regard to this which the employees must be careful to follow.

WHAT IS LIABILITY?

In cases of negligence and malpractice, the person who actually committed the wrong act is held responsible by the law. If that person is an employee of a hospital or clinic or group of doctors, the employer can also be held responsible, provided that the wrongdoing occurred during the employee's working hours in the course of his regular duties. That is, the patient can collect money damages from both the employee and the employer. Ultimately, however, the employee is responsible, for the employer has the right to collect from him any money paid out because of the lawsuit.

Because the professional members of the hospital staff have the greatest responsibility in a patient's care, they are more liable to lawsuits for negligence or malpractice. For this reason it is important for them to carry professional liability insurance. This insurance will not, however, cover any intentional act of wrongdoing.

SUMMARY

It is possible for those working in the medical environment to make decisions which are legally and ethically right, but which can still be questioned morally. One can only stay close to those truths which seem morally right and good for the patients. Decisions must be made honestly by those responsible for making them, with strength of character and a willingness to make personal sacrifices in the interest of the best possible patient care. Although all employees are constantly making ethical decisions, at all levels of employment it is the responsibility of administrators to be the guide in making right ethical decisions.

Administrators are responsible for seeing that employees are aware of and abide by the law. It is further the professional person's responsibility to protect his patients and himself from illegal situations.

The purpose of the law is to promote the general good by protecting the individual from other individuals, groups, or the state, and vice versa. The term "legal right" is defined to mean that which a person is entitled to have, to do, or to receive from another whose duty is imposed within the limits presented by law. Rights may arise as a consequence of a person's existing as a member of society, as well as being the result of a contract.

A license to practice one's profession is a legal document that permits a person to offer to the public his skills and knowledge.

Every contract, to be enforceable at law, must contain (1) the real consent of both parties, (2) a valid consideration (something of value), (3) a lawful object, (4) competent parties, and (5) the form required by law. A breach of contract is a failure without a legal excuse to perform a promise and this gives rise to the right of legal remedy.

Negligence in law is a civil wrong (tort). It is committed when a person is blameworthy or guilty of doing or omitting to do something which it is his positive duty to do or not to do.

Administrators need to be well aware of laws affecting their institutions and are responsible for educating employees concerning laws of the state that relate to medical care. Verbal and written communication are of definite legal importance.

The tone of voice used by an employee to either a patient or a supervisor could mean the difference between legal complications and lack of them. Personality and good interpersonal relationships are therefore important, not only to doing the job properly but also to minimizing the possibility of legal complications.

If one could keep in mind the words of Kahlil Gibran,[9] he could more conscientiously and morally try to follow his ethical and legal convictions.

> Then a lawyer said, But what of our Laws, master?
> And he answered:
> You delight in laying down laws,
> Yet you delight more in breaking them.
> Like children playing by the ocean who build sand-
>   towers with constancy and then destroy them with
>   laughter.

[9] Kahlil Gibran. *The Prophet*. New York: Alfred A. Knopf, 1960, p. 44.

But while you build your sand-towers the ocean brings more sand to the shore,

And when you destroy them the ocean laughs with you.

Verily the ocean laughs always with the innocent.

But what of those to whom life is not an ocean, and man-made laws are not sand-towers,

But to whom life is a rock, and the law a chisel with which they would carve it in their own likeness?

What of the cripple who hates dancers?

What of the ox who loves his yoke and deems the elk and deer of the forest stray and vagrant things?

What of the old serpent who cannot shed his skin, and calls all others naked and shameless?

And of him who comes early to the wedding-feast, and when over-fed and tired goes his way saying that all feasts are violation and all feasters lawbreakers?

What shall I say of these save that they too stand in the sunlight, but with their backs to the sun?

They see only their shadows, and their shadows are their laws.

And what is the sun to them but a caster of shadows?

And what is it to acknowledge the laws but to stoop down and trace their shadows upon the earth?

But you who walk facing the sun, what images drawn on the earth can hold you?

You who travel with the wind, what weather-vane shall direct your course?

What man's law shall bind you if you break your yoke but upon no man's prison door?

What laws shall you fear if you dance but stumble against no man's iron chains?

And who is he that shall bring you to judgment if you tear off your garment yet leave it in no man's path?

People of Orphalese, you can muffle the drum, and you can loosen the strings of the lyre, but who shall command the skylark not to sing?

Bibliography

American College of Hospital Administrators and American Hospital Association. *Code of Ethics.* Chicago: American Hospital Association, 1957.

Black, Henry C. *Black's Law Dictionary.* St. Paul: West Publishing Co., 1933.

Blumel, C. S. "Ethics and Public Relations. The Physician's Responsibility to Patients and to Himself." *Rocky Mountain Medical Journal,* **58:** 32–36, 1961.

Cabot, Richard. *The Meaning of Right and Wrong.* New York: The Macmillan Co., 1933.

Creighton, Helen. "Law for Physical Therapists," *The Physical Therapy Review,* **38:** 22, 93, 165, 251, 1958.

Gibran, Kahlil. *The Prophet.* New York: Alfred A. Knopf, 1960.

Moore, Dom Thomas Vernon. *Principles of Ethics.* Philadelphia: J. B. Lippincott Co., 1943.

Regan, Louis J. *Doctor and Patient and the Law,* 3rd ed. St. Louis: C. V. Mosby Co., 1956.

Smith, T. V., and William Debbins. *Constructive Ethics.* New York: Prentice-Hall, Inc., 1948.

Chapter 7

Personality and Interpersonal Relations in the Medical Environment

Personality plays an important part in anyone's success and happiness in any profession. Personality is particularly important in the medical profession since sick or injured people become frightened and dependent on those caring for them. They need assurance from people they can respect and trust. It is therefore necessary for medical personnel to reflect strength of character, self-assurance, and knowledge of their special profession, as well as to show compassion, empathy, and concern for the immediate needs of the patient.

The personality of any one human being is reflected through the senses of the observer. It consists of the outward impression that human behavior makes on other people.[1] In some ways this outward behavior does not necessarily reflect the inner self, for one could feel an inner insecurity yet put forth quite an act of assurance. This sort of "acting," however, is not very successful and is likely to wear thin. It is obvious that it is best for people working in the medical profession to develop their inner self to

[1] Luella J. Morrison and Mary Agnes Farris. *Approaches for Co-workers in Professional Nursing.* St. Louis: C. V. Mosby Co., 1962, p. 23.

the point where it is compatible with the kind of outer self necessary to work well with patients and co-workers.

Before any employee can understand administrative behavior it is of utmost importance that he understand himself. With self-understanding as a base he is then prepared to analyze his own reactions to administrative decisions. This chapter will discuss development of the inner and outer self as it relates to better working relations with patients, co-workers, and administration.

WHAT IS MEANT BY THE "INNER SELF"?

According to A. H. Maslow,[2] everyone has an inner nature which is intrinsic, given, and unique to the individual. Biologists claim that the possibility of identical twins being wholly alike is one chance to all the electrons in the world.[3] Maslow feels that this inner nature is the true self. It is therefore wise to "listen" to the inner nature and encourage it rather than to suppress it. This inner nature is weak and delicate and easily overcome by habit and cultural and environmental pressure. However, even though weak, it never disappears. It is forever pressing for actualization. If self-actualization is allowed, the person becomes healthy, fruitful, and happy.

Mortimer Adler feels that the soul, spirit, psyche—whatever one chooses to call the inner self—is an attribute of living things. It bears an innate relationship to free motion. Psychic life develops through motion of change for a reason and with a purpose. Psychic life is directed toward an end and involves striving to adapt to environment, striving toward an objective. "We cannot think, feel, will or act," says Adler, "without the perception of some goal." [4]

2 A. H. Maslow. *The Self: Exploration in Personal Growth.* New York: Harper and Brothers, 1956, p. 232.

3 Wilfred A. Peterson. *The Art of Living.* New York: Simon and Schuster, 1961, p. 14.

4 Marie Beynon Ray. *The Importance of Feeling Inferior.* New York: Harper and Brothers, 1957, p. 44.

WHAT IS MEANT BY SUSCEPTIBILITY TO ENVIRONMENT?

If this essential core is denied or suppressed, the person becomes physically or emotionally ill, for the inner nature is subtle and easily overcome by pressures imposed by social customs which create wrong attitudes toward it.[5] Carl Jung emphasizes the need for man, as a social being, to relate to his environment. He feels that the individual will never find real justification for his own existence and his own spiritual and moral anatomy anywhere except in an extramundane principle capable of relativizing the overpowering influence of external factors. The individual needs the evidence of inner transcendent experience to protect him from inevitable submersion into the mass.[6]

A typical example of how easily one can be influenced to join in lazy solutions in order to be compatible with co-workers is the young professional who has learned as a student the ideal ways of using his knowledge and professional skills. He is, however, quickly disillusioned as he sees other people all around him satisfied with giving mediocre patient care. He finds in many instances that he does not have the ideal equipment he learned about in school, and he also finds himself trapped by communication frustrations which inhibit his complete understanding of the situation. All too often it is easier to give up and behave as those around him do rather than strive for better ways of functioning. Or he struggles briefly with what he feels are good suggestions, only to find them rejected by administrators who are unwilling to change patterns of behavior that are traditional to the institution. He then gives up and blends into the environment as an outward peaceful solution rather than taking a strong stand for what his inner self thinks is right.

[5] Maslow, *op. cit.*, p. 232.
[6] Carl G. Jung. *The Undiscovered Self*. New York: The New American Library of World Literature, 1959, p. 34.

It takes a great deal of patience, maturity, and courage to keep working toward new activities and mastering new techniques. Enthusiasm, friendliness, joy, inspiration, motivation, tact, patience, warmth, optimism, reliability, and a never-ending faith in one's own convictions are necessary to avoid stagnation of one's inner self.[7] It is therefore a constant ongoing process to find out what the self is really like, deep down, and to be as true to that *self* as possible.

HOW CAN ONE FOSTER SELF-DEVELOPMENT?

The individual is constantly influencing what he will later become by every response he makes. Each response can strengthen habits which are either good or bad. A weak decision weakens the inner self. Most people live below their highest notch of clearness and discernment, sureness of reasoning, or firmness of decision. Compared with what they potentially *could* be they are only half awake.[8] It is common knowledge that no one is perfect. Knowing one's own weaknesses is a starting point for self-acceptance. This does not mean that the individual must stand in his own shadow, for it is entirely possible to stride forward through one's strengths. It is every individual's responsibility to know both his strengths and weaknesses; to know what he believes is his relation to the universe; to understand his spiritual heritage and from these establish his own aims and purposes toward which he constantly strives.

Setting goals that are too high and therefore unobtainable or expecting to reform the environment toward one's own individual goals will lead only to frustration. True peacefulness of soul will reflect itself through responsiveness to patients. Strength of character will develop more completely through gen-

[7] Helen Hickey. "A Kit of Tools," *Physical Therapy Review*, 31 (No. 4): 135–38, 1951.

[8] Virginia Voeks. *On Becoming an Educated Person*. Philadelphia: W. B. Saunders Co., 1959, p. 20.

tleness to one's self and learning to love the self and to forgive the self, for only if one has the right attitude toward himself can he have the right attitude toward others, and when working with patients the right attitude toward others is of utmost importance.[9]

True self-actualization cannot exist until the individual's background is rich in the gratification of certain basic needs, namely, physical satisfactions, safety, love, and esteem. Since not all of these are readily realized most people exist in varying states of happiness or unhappiness in relationship to the opportunity to satisfy these basic needs. When one has been able to do so to a satisfactory level, he becomes more efficient in his perception of reality. Spontaneity of awareness of the inner life, thoughts, and impulses increases. Interest in solving problems outside himself increases because he is less absorbed with inner self problems. He is freer to do productive, scientific, artistic, or organizational work. He develops a quality of detachment, a need for privacy, and an independence of culture and environment. He has a continued freshness of appreciation. Often he experiences feelings of limitless horizons—a feeling of being simultaneously more powerful and also more helpless than he ever was before.[10]

ONLY BY DOING CAN ONE BECOME

One cannot strive to accumulate wisdom and tranquility elsewhere than in daily encounters with life. Individuals do not develop a philosophy of life through isolated meditation or reading alone. Only through living, moment by moment, and weaving what one *believes* into everything that one *does* can he become the self-actualizing person he hopes to be. Personal experience

[9] Peterson, *op. cit.*, pp. 14–15.
[10] A. H. Maslow. *Motivation and Personality*. New York: Harper and Brothers, 1954, Chap. XII.

quickens the mind and emotions into action. Through bravely expressing one's own emotions rather than those considered conventionally appropriate, strength of character develops. One should beware of taking himself too seriously. The problem is not to become self-conscious dissectors of life, substituting *recipes* for living and loving in place of *living* and *loving*. Goethe pointed out this danger more than a century ago. The real meaning of self-knowledge lies in taking notice of oneself in relation to other people and to the world.[11] One way of expressing the type of love needed by people working with patients could be as follows: [12]

1. The sons of men are one and I am one with them.
   I seek to love, not hate;
   I seek to serve and not exact due service;
   I seek to heal, not hurt.

2. Let pain bring due reward of light and love.
   Let the soul control the outer form,
   and bring to light the love
   Which underlies the happenings of the time.

3. Let vision come and insight.
   Let the future stand revealed.
   Let inner union demonstrate and outer cleavages
      be gone.
   Let love prevail.
   Let all men love!

Every employee's reaction toward administrators will, of course, depend directly on the personalities of the people involved and their ability to adjust to each other. However, the reaction of the new employee will depend greatly on his own inner self, his strengths, or his insecurities.

[11] Laura Archera Huxley. *You Are Not the Target.* New York: Farrar, Straus and Co., 1963, p. 32.

[12] World Goodwill, 866 United Nations Plaza, Suite 566–7, New York, N.Y. 10017.

To illustrate the variety of mixed emotions felt by young people preparing to enter various branches of the medical profession, the following questions were asked of students over a four-year period. Not all the questions were asked of every group; since they stimulated discussion in the dormitories with underclassmen, there was the possibility that some answers could reflect answers of previous upper-class students rather than the student's own thinking.

Who are you? What are you like—deep down inside? What means the most to you? What are your weaknesses? What are your strengths? Why do you think you will do well working in the medical profession? What will working in the medical profession mean to you? What matters most to you as you think about your whole life ahead? What do you want to become and to do with your life? In other words, what is your goal in life? Why did you select this goal? What influences are most important to you as you make decisions and choices that are important to you? What do you have to give to the world, to your country, to your community, and to your family? What do you need in order to reach your goal? What sacrifices are you willing to make for it, and what do you expect or want in return? It is said there is only one aristocracy, the aristocracy of the mind, and one race, the human race. Do you agree? Why? What influence do you hope your life will have on the attitudes and actions of others? In other words, what do you really want your life to count for? [13]

These questions were asked on the first day of classes and without previous reading assignments or discussions in order to assure answers which were not influenced by previous readings or class discussion, eliminating as much as possible quoting from readings or trying to say what the student thought the instructor wanted to hear. Students were also asked not to sign their

[13] Adapted from questions used by Esther Alice Beard in *Toward Understanding People: A Study of the Insights and Goals of College Students Preparing to Teach.* New York: Teachers College, Columbia University, 1959, pp. 8–9 (mimeographed dissertation).

names in a further attempt to obtain reliable reflections of a true analysis of themselves. The students enjoyed this exercise and approached these assignments eagerly. Answers to these questions indicated as many personalities as there were people questioned! Therefore, the number of possible reactions to administrative personalities is immense.

One answered the question, "What are you like deep down inside," saying, "Deep down inside I have a definite set of morals and values. I can adjust very readily and do not need a period to become used to new situations." Another replied, "This question is unanswerable without many hours of thinking. In my way I'm like hundreds of others but I like to feel that I am also set apart from them." Another replied, "I desire to treat others with dignity and respect, never degrading another as a means to my own goals. To strive to make a contribution to my society that will aid my fellow man. Give of myself and expect nothing in return and by so doing gain a respect and development of intrinsic self."

Answers such as these reflect maturity and a certain faith in the self that in all probability would enable the person to understand administrative personalities and strive to understand the total situation before reacting to it emotionally. Many students expressed anxiety and insecurity saying, "Deep down inside I'm nervous about many things," or "Inside I'm confused and worried," or "Lots of times I'm quite unhappy, but try to cover it up by acting happy," or "Deep down, I am an entirely different person than what shows outwardly. I don't know if this is good but I manage to keep happy. Inside I worry but I have learned to keep smiling and 'think love' realizing that big mountains are not conquered alone." Another said, "Deep down inside I feel I am very humble and have a great inferiority complex which I cover up by behaving conceited or overly confident." Still another said, "It is difficult to say what I am really deep down inside because often I don't like to think about it so deeply. I am very undecided and confused."

WHAT ARE FAVORABLE AND UNFAVORABLE RESPONSES?

Most of these expressions of insecurity will probably exist within these people as they approach their first job. Their view of administrators is not likely to be on an eye-to-eye level, but rather with a "Please tell me what you want and I'll try to do it" attitude. It is quite obvious that most of these people are sincerely anxious to succeed at varying levels of maturity within themselves. Depending on their ability to see administrative problems and to identify the reasons behind administrative decisions, young workers may strive to understand the situation. If they disagree with administrative decisions, and if they are truly immature, they may show resentment or anger before they have sufficiently explored the total situation enough to completely understand it.

Many young staff members prefer to ignore administrators' feelings, assuming that their only job is to fulfill their own assignments. They are unwilling or afraid to make suggestions. It often takes a new person at least a year (sometimes more) to become well enough acquainted with the organization to "fit in" and work comfortably and without frustration, fulfilling himself and forwarding the objectives of the organization. Administrative problems can be greatly increased by extremes, and these extremes are common, owing either to insecurity or to overconfidence on the part of young or new employees. They are often either frustated by situations that seem to have no solutions or they "settle down" and decide to "live with" problems that could be solved. Favorable responses from new employees would include questioning less than ideal situations; offering suggestions; listening to reasons why these suggestions had failed in the past; yet continuing to try to find solutions without being critical of the present.

As young employees see these problems their first reaction is to be critical; to sit at "curbstone conferences" and over cigarettes and coffee breaks and talk among themselves, relieving some of their own tensions by discussing and verbalizing what they would *do* if they were their immediate supervisor or administrator. They would make better use of their time if they would study the structure of present society, both the immediate society of their organization and the broader society in which they live. If courses were not offered to them concerning psychologic and social needs of the entire hospital staff, they should request inservice education that would help them understand such problems as shortage of personnel, the organization of their institution, and better methods of working with staff groups.[14] Many times such assistance is requested but without follow-up. Young staff members could turn "gripe sessions" into constructive group therapy by self-planned meetings where, at each meeting, one person reports on a contemporary book that deals with their particular problem. This encourages integration of thoughts by bringing differences into the open. One such group met every day during their lunch hour (in a crowded dining room) using a brief report on some book dealing with mutual problems as a starting point for opening positive and constructive discussions for better ways to solve their dilemmas. At the end of two weeks the group had identified with each other's problems to the point where relationships were so strong and mutual understanding so real that they felt reluctant to discontinue the experiment.

One hospital attempted to encourage greater understanding among all hospital personnel by *not* having separate dining rooms for doctors, hoping that clique and hierarchy groups would intermingle. The experiment failed utterly because hierarchical groups refused to sit apart and simply "took over" certain sections of the dining room while those further down the ladder sat in their own corners and talked with people in their own departments.

To work well in the medical environment the individual needs

[14] Esther Lucile Brown. *Newer Dimensions of Patient Care,* Part 2. New York: Russell Sage Foundation, 1961, p. 3.

the *Gemeinschaftsgefuhl:* that deep feeling of identification, sympathy, and affection for mankind as a whole. He needs deep and profound understanding of interpersonal relations and a stong faith in the democratic character structure. He needs to be able to discriminate between the means and the ends. A philosophic, nonhostile sense of humor is absolutely essential. He needs creativeness and an inner resistance to complete conformity with cultural and environmental standards.[15] Certain imperfections are bound to exist and no one individual could qualify highly on all of these idealistic character traits suggested by Maslow. They do provide a few stars to reach for and, if obtainable in any degree, would certainly lead toward understanding patients and working with them with a spirit of "togetherness" in the daily life of professional activities with a minimum of friction or frustration for the patient.

Aside from the understanding, empathy, and concern for the patient's welfare, it is often the actual things that personnel can *do* for the patient that reflect their desire to aid the patient. There are so many other ways to communicate than through words: use of facial expressions, gestures, written notes, or other methods of personal contact.[16] The way the patient is touched when contact is necessary or helpful, an encouraging pat on the shoulder, a gentle touch while bathing or turning the patient, special care when certain treatments cause pain are all communication without words that show concern for the patient. Take, for example, the case of a woman who had been struck between the eyes with a golf ball, causing severe fractures to the area and a great deal of bleeding which ran into her hair. She lay blinded by swelling and congestion, trying patiently to exist until the healing process could proceed to the point where she could leave the hospital. Three or four days after the accident an aide asked her if she weren't miserable with all that dried blood in her hair. The patient of course said "Yes," but had assumed it

[15] Maslow, *op. cit.,* Chap. XII.
[16] Donna Yancey. "Without Words," *American Journal of Nursing,* **62:** 118–19, 1962.

must be endured. It took the aide two hours of painstakingly soaking a few strands of hair at a time in warm water to get the hair washed without touching or disturbing the injured area. The fact that someone *cared* meant more to the patient than the comfort that followed the careful shampoo.

It is fortunate that most people who want to work in a hospital do so because they are truly interested in caring for patients. Dissatisfaction on the part of the *patient* often arises from the fact that personnel are too busy to give every patient the full attention he needs for full emotional support. The best that those who care for the patient can do is try at all times to "listen," not only to what the patient *says,* but to try to know how the patient's inner self is feeling and to try to preserve the patient's image of himself as an individual.

PATIENTS HAVE INNER SELVES ALSO!

In working with patients it is important for all employees to remember that patients have inner selves also. Under most circumstances when the patient is moved from his home to the hospital his own resources for self-expression and self-actualization are almost completely eliminated. His self-image undergoes immediate assault as he finds himself helplessly confronted with people dressed in white who now begin to rule his life. He sees the physician as all-powerful and the head nurse as boss of the place. Even aides and orderlies find themselves in a position to grant or withhold what are really small, but now become to the patient precious, favors. On this basis the social characteristics of the hospital tend to stimulate a considerable amount of dread and apprehension on the part of the patient. Some treatments can amount to actual torture and are often given without explanation, leaving the patient with misgivings and hostility against a necessary procedure. Anxious personal feelings between the patient and hospital staff develop.[17] It is highly im-

17 Brown, *op. cit.,* pp. 122–23.

portant for all personnel who have direct contact with the patient to try to overcome these apprehensions by first *being* the supportive empathetic and understanding person patients need. Empathy is akin to sympathy, the difference being that sympathy says, "I feel as you do," while empathy says, "I *know* how you feel." Empathy involves using the head more than the heart. It requires imagination. One must either know from experience or be able to imagine onself in the situation of the other person.[18] The hospital employee must consciously and constantly and deliberately "tune in" on the feelings of the patients, trying to know at all times how *they* are reacting to their experience in the hospital. Many aides and orderlies succeed highly in giving understanding and warmth, for they are often close to the patient throughout his daily activities while head nurses and doctors seem more remote to the patient.

If a patient becomes angry, upset, frustrated, confused, or depressed, personnel must realize that it is their responsibility to comfort the patient and must realize that all patients are uprooted from their whole pattern of living temporarily and are therefore at a disadvantage. The more enlightened patient can be the most difficult one to deal with. They say doctors and nurses are often the worst patients, for they find it difficult to adjust to the sudden switch in role. While they once guided patients' every moves, now they are being restricted, instructed, and denied "privileges."

WHY DOES IMPERSONALITY OFTEN EXIST?

The actual *real* showing of compassion and empathy to the patient often gets lost because of several factors. Medical personnel are often not well enough acquainted with the patient to know his individual doubts and fears and therefore are not aware of his particular needs. The rigid rules of the hospital of-

[18] R. W. Armstrong. "Empathy," *Nursing Times,* **52**: 1006–9, 1956.

ten bring personal psychologic suffering to the patient, who misses his family and the comforts of home—a cup of coffee when he feels like having it, his children playing near him in the same room, his own hobbies, such as playing the organ or puttering in his shop. Robbed of these he has every reason to become irritable—not to mention his apprehension at the outcome of the many examinations to which he is usually subjected.

The necessity for hospitals to have rather rigid standard procedures and the dual purpose of patient care and management of a large business enterprise often bring about reduced personal contact between staff members and patients. Depersonalization of the hospital patient begins on admission. Just as a factory changes raw materials into a form in which they can be handled by machines, the hospital transforms the incoming "sick" person into a patient by placing him in a standard setting, putting him into hospital clothes, and molding his dietary and sleep habits by standardized eating and sleeping times.[19] Custodial demands on the staff to accomplish certain tasks on a given shift force the patient to conform to the routine of the hospital. The pressures on the staff to get their assigned work done tends to depersonalize their relation with the patient since their major goal is task-oriented, and within their own consciousness they are thinking primarily of "getting all the beds made by ten o'clock before the supervisor arrives," rather than having any real concern for the sick bodies in the beds they are making.

Staff members also tend to develop impersonality toward patients through a subconscious need to buffer themselves against the almost overwhelming exposure to suffering, pain, anxiety, tension, and tragedy. To identify with it too closely would be unbearable for the inner self to accept. Thus there exists in most hospital personnel the conflicting forces of the conscious need and desire to develop personal rapport with the patients and the

[19] E. Goffman. "Characteristics of Total Institutions," in M. R. Stein, A. J. Vidich, and D. M. White (eds.). *Identity and Anxiety: Survival of the Person in Mass Society.* New York: Free Press of Glencoe, 1960.

countering pressures toward impersonality and social distance from the patient.[20]

WHY IS IT NECESSARY TO WORK WELL WITH CO-WORKERS?

Working under the conditions so far described it is obvious that a great deal of give and take is necessary. Luella Morrison and Mary Agnes Farris describe this as one's GAT ratio.[21] One must give of himself to other people who are willing to receive what he has to offer. To keep the GAT ratio in balance one must also be equally ready to receive what other people have to offer. In working well with co-workers one must accept the fact that life is a series of experiences. Growth toward maturity and satisfaction from work experiences depend on how each experience is accepted, for every experience influences the individual in some way, be it pain, fear, or unhappiness. Each experience needs analysis to determine what it means to the inner self. Often traumatic experiences result in ultimate growth of spirit when the analysis indicates to the individual that he can do better next time. In order to understand each other, employees must have a clear idea of the job that needs to be accomplished. Since situations are no more perfect than people, a certain GAT ratio is necessary in order to anticipate how well or thoroughly a job can be done with the present equipment and in the given length of time. The employee who is constantly critical of his administrator because the job is not always perfectly done only makes himself unhappy because he does not possess enough give and take to realize that other outside factors beyond the administrator's control have prevented the job from going as well as had been anticipated.

Employees need to understand each other whenever two people work together. They must know what the other person is try-

[20] Lawrence E. Schlesinger. "Staff Tensions and Needed Skills in Staff-Patient Interactions," *Rehabilitation Literature*, **24:** 362, 1963.

[21] Morrison and Farris, *op. cit.*, p. 51.

ing to accomplish. They must talk to each other, write to each other, or by any other means get their ideas from one to the other. In the medical environment this communication is very important and often must be quick for the welfare of the patient.

General Motors once found that it took a year before a decision made by the board of directors found its way down to its actual application in the shop. A worker sarcastically rejoined, "And how long does it take for an idea of one of the men in the shop to find its way to the board of directors?" Patients cannot afford to wait a year before some communication concerning their welfare reaches its necessary destination.

The average employee wants to enjoy a sense of belonging. He takes pride in doing his work well and responds to a little word of praise for a job well done. Most hospital employees are not so concerned about the amount of money they make as they are about pleasant and satisfying working conditions. The lowest manual worker is all aglow with pride if he is complimented. Any employee wants to know why he is being asked to do a certain task, and when he asks, he deserves an explanation. If he understands what is going on, he is usually anxious to cooperate. Few employees work alone in hospital situations. Their duties overlap. Everything they do relates to the patient and usually overlaps with one or more of the other hospital departments. Although there are certain teams such as nursing or rehabilitation that are clearly organized, there are still further interlocking relations with the medical staff, the directing staff, and many other departments of the hospital. Under these circumstances "togetherness" is a must.

This constant group activity requires that all members of the group have an understanding of personal interaction among human beings. One way for on-the-job learning to work well is for supervisors to provide opportunities for learners to study and work together. Assignments of committees to study projects will develop desirable attitudes as well as inform as many people as possible about existing problems.[22] Informal discussions can be held to exchange concepts that may be misconcepts, strengthening the group through the development of unity of information. Benefits to all those working together will result as the members with more practical experience discuss possibilities for action with younger and less experienced people.

SUMMARY

Personality is as important as knowledge and skill. Without a suitable personality a person who stands at the top of the class academically can fail miserably because of an inability to work smoothly in the medical environment. The personality needed to work in medical institutions requires strength of character and self-assurance. It must be able to show compassion, empathy, and concern for the immediate needs of the patient.

Everyone has an inner nature which is intrinsic, given, and unique to that individual. This inner self constantly strives for actualization and must have this in order for the person to become healthy, fruitful, and happy. This essential core is delicate and subtle and can be easily overcome by environmental pressure. It is therefore a constant responsibility to the self to evaluate how one feels deep down and decide to be true to that inner self. The inner self should grow with every experience in order for the individual to live to his highest notch of discernment.

Self-acceptance, knowing one's strengths and one's weaknesses, knowing what one believes in give him a base to establish his own aims and purposes toward which he constantly strives. True peacefulness of soul will reflect itself through responsiveness toward patients. Strength of character comes from loving and forgiving one's self. He must learn this before he can

[22] Lester Crow and Alice Crow. *Understanding Interrelations in Nursing.* New York: The Macmillan Co., 1961, p. 77.

love and forgive others. Self-actualization allows one to find interest in solving problems outside himself. Only by *doing* can one *become*.

In their relationship to patients employees need a deep feeling of identification, sympathy, and affection for mankind as a whole, a deep and profound understanding of interpersonal relations, and a strong faith in the democratic character structure. Most people work in a hospital because they are truly interested in helping patients. They will be better able to serve the patients if they strive to understand how the patient's inner self is feeling, for patients have inner selves too. When the patient is hospitalized his ability for self-actualization is strongly inhibited as he becomes fearful and frustrated. Hospital personnel must realize their responsibility in overcoming these fears and striving to indicate personal concern for the patient's welfare to avoid depersonalization.

Since so many people work together, the GAT (give-and-take) ratio is of utmost importance for individuals and groups who work together in the interest of the best possible patient care. The employee who is constantly critical of his administrator because things don't seem to be running smoothly makes himself unhappy if his GAT ratio does not help him realize that factors beyond the administrator's control have prevented the job from going as well as had been anticipated.

The average employee wants to enjoy a sense of belonging. He takes pride in doing his work well and responds warmly to praise. He expects his administrator to explain to him why he is asked to do a certain task. When he understands he is willing to cooperate. The constant interlocking of activities between people and between departments demands a great deal of "togetherness." Opportunities for group discussions and committee study of problems should be provided. Informal discussions for exchanging information should occur as often as possible.

The self-actualizing person will gladly, and with deliberate and full consciousness of all that he is doing, subordinate his own personality to the good of the whole with a gentle love for the self and others, through freely expressing empathy and compassion first for the patient, but also for his fellow workers. Those who succeed best will take emerging ideas and, through group activity, materialize them, synthesizing human endeavor and expressing truer values leading to the best possible patient care.

Bibliography

Armstrong, R. W. "Empathy," *Nursing Times,* **52:** 1006, 1956.

Beard, Esther Alice. *Toward Understanding People: A Study of the Insights and Goals of College Students Preparing to Teach.* New York: Teachers College, Columbia University, 1959. (Mimeographed dissertation.)

Brown, Esther Lucile. *Newer Dimensions in Patient Care,* Part 1. New York: Russell Sage Foundation, 1961.

Crow, Lester, and Alice Crow. *Understanding Interrelations in Nursing.* New York: The Macmillan Co., 1961.

Goffman, E. "Characteristics of Total Institutions," in M. R. Stein, A. J. Vidich, and D. M. White (eds.). *Identity and Anxiety: Survival of the Person in Mass Society.* New York: Free Press of Glencoe, 1960.

Hickey, Helen. "A Kit of Tools," *Physical Therapy Review,* **31** (No. 4): 135, 1951.

Huxley, Laura Archera. *You Are Not the Target.* New York: Farrar, Straus and Co., 1963.

Jung, Carl G. *The Undiscovered Self.* New York: The New American Library of World Literature, 1959.

Maslow, A. H. *Motivation and Personality.* New York: Harper and Brothers, 1954.

———. *The Self: Exploration in Personal Growth.* New York: Harper and Brothers, 1956.

Morrison, Luella J., and Mary Agnes Farris. *Approaches for Coworkers in Professional Nursing.* St. Louis: C. V. Mosby Co., 1962.

Peterson, Wilfred A. *The Art of Living*. New York: Simon and Schuster, 1961.

Ray, Marie Beynon. *The Importance of Feeling Inferior*. New York: Harper and Brothers, 1957.

Schlesinger, Lawrence E. "Staff Tensions and Needed Skills in Staff-Patient Interactions," *Rehabilitation Literature,* 24: 362, 1963.

Voeks, Virginia. *On Becoming an Educated Person*. Philadelphia: W. B. Saunders Co., 1959.

Yancey, Donna. "Without Words," *American Journal of Nursing,* **62:** 118, 1962.

PART II

CASES

Introduction

This part presents cases that deal with many of the problems discussed in Part I. Each case relates to one or more of the problems that exist in administration in the hospital.

Part I described the organizational setting of the hospital and presented an explanation of the administrative structure and interpersonal relations that frequently exist within the hospital environment to show the kinds of situations that create these problems. Part I also suggested ways in which an informed person can assist to alleviate these problems.

All the following cases present problems, simple or complex, which require the reader to do some creative thinking. This arouses the interest of the reader. It makes him an active rather than a passive participant in the learning process. He relates theory to practice as he thinks purposefully about the facts presented to him.

The purpose of using case material in teaching is to help individuals study questions related to actual situations. It helps to break down traditional barriers between theory and practice since the topics of discussion are based on real experiences.

The heart of this method lies in helping participants to think in ways that are productive in the hospital environment. Case material brings real situations to inexperienced people for discussion. It keeps the subject alive and in tune with current problems. Attention is focused on what people need to know in order to function in their positions. Use of the case method is democratic rather than dictatorial. It encourages independent thinking.

When people study and discuss case material, they must do more than read facts in textbooks or absorb them from lectures. More careful preparation is required for discussions. Lectures, preparatory readings, and assignments must be studied. The discussion of cases provides the advantage of "on-the-spot" thinking. Activity is then primarily the participant's responsibility. Although right decisions are important results of discussions, the *process* of thinking, not the decision itself, is the important end result. The use of the case method can be a means for putting vitality and sharper meaning into professional education.

Before a person can participate in the solution of problems existing in his job, he should have confidence in his own competence, in his ideas, and in expressing them. The discussion of cases helps him to develop analytic and critical abilities as well as creativity. He must know when to look for facts, where to find them, and how to share them with others. He begins to realize that others in similar situations have needs to be understood and accepted just as he has. He learns to defend his values and is willing to modify them. He begins to learn that disagreement grows out of misunderstanding. A discussion group can give people practice in human relations skills.

Discussion in a group has many values which are related to emotional gratification, self-esteem, and personality growth of the members of the group. This method of teaching cannot be successful without the participant first preparing himself by studying background material related to the case at hand. Cases should be studied ahead of time, for thought and consideration. In attempting to analyze the cases, people should first study the basic principles which the case involves, by referring to Part I and outside reading material suggested by the references provided with each case. Following this, people should study the cases and respond to them, solve the problem, and make their own evaluation of the situation.

Groups frequently feel confused when they first attempt to use the case method since it does not supply them with pat answers to the problems. This confusion is soon replaced through good leadership and by interest and enthusiasm. In the hands of an experienced leader, large groups can be divided, and, after a short time, reconvened for discussion. Those too shy to speak before the larger group participate more freely in the smaller group. This method also brings out more ideas for the total group discussion.

Did you ever feel like a mosquito in a nudist colony . . . knowing what had to be done, but not able to decide where to begin?

Mr. Billings' Annual Report

As Mr. Billings walked to work he meditated upon the report he would soon be making to the board of directors. The Harris Memorial Hospital, of which he was administrator, was in transition, growing from a relatively small to a medium-sized hospital. Certain parts of the renovation were already completed and in use. The kitchen had received an entirely new look; there were new lighting and new ventilation, and the rearrangement of equipment, old and new, made it more functional. In the x-ray department there was a fine new waiting room with comfortable chairs and lounges. Soft lights and even soft music were now provided to ease the concern of patients who waited anxiously for the results of their x-rays. Formerly patients had been forced to sit in the hallway, often as long as an hour, either in their wheelchairs or on straight, wooden chairs.

Improvements were coming about as the result of a very successful fund-raising campaign. Although the renovation program posed many financial problems, Mr. Billings felt he could assure the board of directors that the hospital was on a sound financial basis because adequate programs had been and would be devised to meet the ever-increasing costs of medical care in terms of both personnel and equipment. More efficient patient care could be anticipated with these new facilities and equipment. There should be an increasing rapport with those for whom and by whom the hospital existed, namely, the patients. Inservice education included classes at the top management level: active research was being done in housekeeping, and a study was being made of the needs of the operating suite and central sterile supply. In nursing, a committee that would serve on a continuing basis had set up a basic procedure book. An inservice education program for nurses' aides was offered.

Mr. Billings felt that his report should give credit to all department heads for being constantly restless and self-critical in the effort to produce better service. As he approached his office, his thoughts turned toward future goals that should be summarized. The hospital needed a broader base for financing its growth. He could suggest a monthly public relations tour as a method for educating the public to services and costs. He tried to think of other ways to increase communication between the hospital and the community it served. It was difficult for the people of this small, industrial town to understand that adequate facilities could be obtained only through their donations or through increased hospital fees.

Finally settled in his office, Mr. Billings began to write his report. Before long he had an uneasy feeling that his words were too glowing. A phone call from his chief resident, complaining that a patient with a suspected malignancy was being forced to wait a month before there would be a bed for her at the hospital, reminded him that even with the new wing, this small hospital caused heartbreak owing to its overcrowded conditions. A complaint from the kitchen that one of the cooks had gotten into a fistfight with one of the orderlies made him realize that in a small community it was difficult to obtain good employees at the nonprofessional level. Whether he liked to admit it or not, he realized that often nurses' aides were doing some of the duties that nurses should be doing.

Mr. Billings decided that it might be a good idea to take a tour of the hospital before finishing his report in order to make it more realistic. He first visited the chief of the medical staff to find out more about the patient who would have to wait for admission. He found that Miss Young was a teacher in their community, who was seeing her doctor because of abdominal discomfort. Some years previously she had a hysterectomy for a malignant tumor and had been advised by her doctors that she needed regular checkups to see that there was no return of this malignancy. Now her doctor thought there might be a recurrence. When she learned she would have to wait a month for further tests, she became very apprehensive and began to weep. She explained to her doctor that she did not want to wait a month to know whether she was going to live or die and begged him for tranquilizers or something that would help her through the next few weeks until she could be admitted to the hospital. In his attempts to soothe her the doctor said, "Well, you know, Miss Young, it isn't as if it were acute appendicitis, This is something that can wait and only great emergencies can be admitted." Mr. Billings doubted that this made Miss Young feel better.

Mr. Billings next went to the x-ray department where he saw two patients in wheelchairs with their orderlies waiting in the hall. Another young man dressed in white was sitting with them smoking and chatting pleasantly. This reminded him of the constant problem they had with the orderlies who were prone to waste much of their time talking and smoking with the patients. He decided to act immediately. Walking up to the fellow he said, "I am Mr. Billings, the hospital administrator. What should you be doing instead of sitting here smoking and talking with the patients?"

The surprised young man was at a loss for words as he wondered what else he should be doing. Before he could think of an answer, an x-ray technician stepped out saying, "We are ready for you now, Mr. Fitzgerald." Mr Billings realized he had mistaken a patient for an orderly. He wondered momentarily whether to apologize or not, but he decided to let it go, hoping that Mr. Fitzgerald would understand.

Mr. Billings looked about and noticed other patients waiting unattended in the hallway. One patient was an old woman of about 90 years who appeared very frail and seemed to find it difficult to sit upright in her chair. Another was a young boy in obvious pain from a broken ankle. He also sat on a straight chair in the hall as he waited for results of his x-rays.

Wondering why these patients were not seated in the new waiting room in a more comfortable environment, Mr. Billings went around the corner into the waiting room where he found several nurses and x-ray technicians smoking and listening to the soothing music intended for the waiting patients. Mr. Billings asked the nurse in charge of the waiting room why all the patients were sitting in the hallway. The surprised nurse and several technicians scurried into the hallway to bring the patients into the waiting room. Discouraged that the new waiting room was not being used for the patients and that the former practice of having patients wait in the hall had been continued, he decided to check again in a few days.

Mr. Billings heard his name being paged and picked up a nearby phone. He was quickly connected with the head nurse on the fifth floor. She begged him to come immediately to see the intolerable conditions which she, her staff, and the patients suffered. As he stepped from the elevator, the loud noises of sledge hammers knocking plaster from a room adjoining the new wing could be heard. Plaster dust filled the air and drifted downward to form thick layers over everything. He could hear violent coughing and on investigation found the cougher was an asthmatic patient. When he asked if this patient could be moved to another floor, he found that no beds were available.

Another patient lay weeping on a bed in the hallway next to the room where the pounding was going on. He asked the head nurse why this patient was weeping. The patient had been hospitalized that morning with a hypertensive crisis. Since no rooms were available, she had been placed in the bed in the hall. Mr. Billings overheard the patient beg to have her bed moved away from the pounding since she had a miserable headache. A passing nurse replied, "No beds can be moved without permission." Mr. Billings moved the bed down the hall a few yards. The head nurse followed him about explaining that this patient had been forced to undress without the aid of screens because none were available. She had also been forced to use the bedpan as work-men passed her bed with dusty loads of plaster. As a result of all this, in spite of medication, her blood pressure was not going down as it should.

Before Mr. Billings could think of a solution, the emergency room called saying that three people had been brought in from an automobile accident. Knowing there were no more rooms available, he asked them to proceed with whatever measures were necessary while he tried to find three patients on the ortho-pedic ward who could be discharged. He called the chief of orthopedic surgery only to find he had gone on a hunting trip leaving his assistant in charge. He called the assistant and was told he was on his way to surgery to care for the three patients in the emergency room. Mr. Billings then went directly to the orthopedic floor to see what preparations could be made. He found that two patients were checking out that afternoon. He made all necessary arrangements for their immediate dismissal and was able to make room for an additional bed in the ward.

By noon Mr. Billings was exhausted and had written nothing on his annual report. He prayed that the new wing could soon be completed and realized that to serve this community there was constantly a need for increased space.

Questions

1. What were Mr. Billings' major administrative problems?

2. What things could he do something about?

3. Were there problems he could do nothing about at the moment? What were they?

4. How could the individual worker have relieved or prevented some of the problems presented in this case?

5. What should Mr. Billings emphasize in his annual report?

References

American College of Hospital Administrators, American Hospital Association. *Code of Ethics*. Chicago: American Hospital Association, 1964, p. 1, "Objectives of the Hospital."

Heneman, Harlow J. "Administrators Waste Time Chasing Details," *The Modern Hospital*, **99**: 87, 1962.

Nadler, Leonard. *Leadership on the Job. Guides to Good Supervision*. New York: American Management Association, 1954.

———. "A Manager's Job Is to Help Employees Grow," *The Modern Hospital*, **95**: 119, 1960.

———. "Small Hospital Questions," *The Modern Hospital*, **95**: 76, 1960.

Platon, Carl. "How to Make Friends with People Before They're Patients," *The Modern Hospital*, **95**: 112, 1960.

Sloan, Raymond P. *Today's Hospital*. New York: Harper and Row, 1966, Chap. 6, "Executive Direction," p. 119.

The hurrier I go, the behinder I get!

Graduate Nurses Meet Reality

Sandra MacDonald and Mary Markland were about to receive their B.S. degrees in nursing from the state university. They had been good friends for four years and each had married men in Danville. Both applied for nursing positions at the Danville Memorial Hospital. Most of their classmates had heard from the hospital where they had applied for positions, but Mrs. MacDonald and Mrs. Markland were still anxiously waiting. The day before graduation both received a mimeographed notice that read:

> You have been accepted for a position on the nursing staff of the Danville Memorial Hospital. Please report for work at 7 A.M., July 1, 1963.

It was signed by Frances Hartley, the director of nursing services. Although other students had received more cordial and personal appointment letters, both girls were pleased to know they had the positions they wanted. They promptly replied that they would report as requested.

At 7 A.M. on July 1, 1963, they arrived at work, spotless in their new whites and eager to launch their careers. They were met by the assistant director of nursing services who first showed them how to punch the time clock. Then she said, "We are so understaffed! I was going to take you for an orientation tour, but Miss Clark needs help so badly I'll have to assign you directly to her."

When they reported to Miss Clark, head nurse for third-floor intermediate care, she was sitting at the nurses' station writing the daily orders for supplies. Miss Clark welcomed them warmly, expressing her relief that she had some help. She showed them the utility and linen rooms, then gave them two books with the names of patients and their room numbers, saying, "While both of you take temperatures, record them, and give the patients their morning wash, I'll finish the orders for supplies and get the charts ready for morning rounds." She sat down and continued her work. Both girls hesitated. Finally Mrs. MacDonald asked, "Where are the thermometers?" Miss Clark looked a little annoyed, but replied, "We keep them in the treatment room."

Mrs. MacDonald took one book and Mrs. Markland the other, and each went about her first assignment. Many questions needed to be asked, but since Miss Clark seemed annoyed and busy, they went about their morning duties as best they could. The room numbers were confusing because they did not run consecutively. They had no idea what was wrong with the patients as they met them and had to rely on the patients to tell them whether they needed a basin or could get to the bathroom to wash.

One patient who concerned Mrs. Markland was Dr. Moore. Since he was an M.D., she wanted to do everything right. She introduced herself and asked what his diagnosis was. He told her he was scheduled for surgery for kidney stones. Mrs. Markland was embarrassed because the washbasin was not in his bedside stand. She looked in the bathroom and did not see it there. Finally she asked Dr. Moore if he had a basin.

"I don't know," he replied. "I've been going into the bathroom, but now that I'm medicated for surgery, I think I should stay in bed." Mrs. Markland finally found a basin in the utility room.

When she went into Mrs. Blair's room, she found the patient sick to her stomach. There was no basin there either; so she used a towel and proceeded to clean up Mrs. Blair and change her bed and nightgown. Mrs. Blair complained of severe nausea. Mrs. Markland reported this incident to Miss Clark and then hurried on with her other duties.

Another patient asked her for mouthwash. After a five-minute fruitless search through the utility room, she had to report to the patient that she could not find any. "Oh," said the patient, "I have my own. It's right in the bathroom."

As soon as they finished "temps and washup," they reported to Miss Clark and waited while she was on the telephone reporting diet changes. Their new orders were: "Mrs. MacDonald, you take the two wards and all treatments ordered for the floor. Mrs. Markland, you take the rest of the patients. Mrs. Blair, Dr. Moore, Mr. Sealey, and Miss Jones need attention first. Be sure Dr. Moore is ready for surgery by nine o'clock." Once again the girls hesitated. "Well, what is it?" asked Miss Clark with a trace of impatience in her voice.

"May we have a report on the patients? We know nothing about any of them," said Mrs. Markland.

"I know I should," said Miss Clark, "but I just haven't time. You'll have to read their charts. If you have any real problems I'll try to help you, but it will be time for rounds soon, and I haven't all the charts ready."

Mrs. MacDonald and Mrs. Markland continued as best they could. As they passed each other in the hall, Mrs. MacDonald said, "How are you doing, Mary?"

Mrs. Markland replied, rolling her eyes skyward, "Vomiting, diarrhea, bedpans, vomiting, diarrhea, bedpans. . . . I can't get to my treatments! Do you know where the sitz bath is?"

"No, but I'll bet the patient does."

"That's a good idea, thanks."

Mrs. Markland was thankful to find that Mrs. Jones knew where the sitz bath was. The patient also knew how to manage the electrical thermostatic control, one that Mrs. Markland had never seen before. Mrs. Markland was dubious about leaving Mrs. Jones to care for herself, but the patient insisted she had done so before.

Mrs. Markland then went to Dr. Moore's room for final preparations for surgery. She was relieved to find him not only jovial but helpful and not too concerned about her insecurities on her first day at work.

When she went to Mr. Sealey's room, he was not in bed. She

knocked at the bathroom door; there was no reply but she heard the sound of running water. She opened the door a crack and could see the slumped form of Mr. Sealey on the bathroom floor. A quick check of his pulse led Mrs. Markland to believe the patient was dead. She rushed to Miss Clark to report this and was amazed at the calmness with which Miss Clark called for Mr. Sealey's physician. Her own heart was pounding, and she felt quite ill. "He probably shouldn't have been out of bed at all," she thought.

Meanwhile, in the ward, Mrs. MacDonald was having a problem with Mr. Meyers, who was hospitalized for surgery to his foot. When Mr. Meyers saw her walking past his bed, he called to her, "Nurse! Nurse! I don't feel so good." Mrs. MacDonald stopped. "I have a terrible pain in my chest and I'm dizzy." Mrs. MacDonald sent a nearby aide for a blood pressure cuff, thinking to herself this would be more efficient than hunting for one herself. While waiting for the equipment, she read the patient's chart and found he did have a history of hypertension. Mr. Meyers' blood pressure was fairly high; so Mrs. MacDonald reported this to Miss Clark and recorded it on the patient's chart. She was surprised when Miss Clark did not seem concerned and did not call Mr. Meyers' doctor.

"Take his blood pressure again in 15 minutes," suggested Miss Clark. "I'll bet it will be back down to normal. Mr. Meyers does this all the time. It's a subconscious way of getting attention." Mrs. MacDonald took his blood pressure in 15 minutes, and it was indeed normal.

During the morning Miss Clark gave medications and often, as she passed the two new nurses, she would cheerfully ask, "How are you doing?" At no time did she interrupt her own duties to assist them in any way. Once when she had just come from Mr. Meyers' room, she stopped Mrs. MacDonald and asked her to take a glass of water to him.

By noon both Mrs. MacDonald and Mrs. Markland had completely changed their ideas about the role of a nurse. They were both physically and emotionally exhausted and confused. They wondered what the afternoon would hold and whether or not they would ever know where to find anything.

Questions

1. What were the obvious personnel problems at Danville Memorial Hospital?

2. Can you identify any organizational problems?

3. Did the situation allow Mrs. MacDonald and Mrs. Markland to act effectively? Could they have acted more wisely?

4. Did Miss Clark need more assistance?

5. Did Miss Clark make the best use of her time?

References

Agnes, Edith A. "Nine Ways to Improve Nursing Service," *The Modern Hospital*, **97**: 112, 1961.

Barabas, Mary Helen. *Contemporary Head Nursing.* New York: The Macmillan Co., 1962, pp. 30–118.

Brackett, Mary E. "What Nurses Dislike about Their Jobs," *The Modern Hospital*, **89**: 53–58, 1957.

Calender, Tiny M. *Unit Administration.* Philadelphia: W. B. Saunders Co., 1962, Chap. 8, "The Head Nurse."

Davis, Fred (ed.). *The Nursing Profession.* New York: John Wiley and Sons, Inc., 1966, Chap. 3, "The Organizational Context of Nursing Practice," p. 109.

Hale, Thomas, Jr. "Why the Nursing Supply Is Failing to Meet the Demand," *The Modern Hospital*, **95**: 100–104, 1960.

Henderson, Virginia. *The Nature of Nursing.* New York: The Macmillan Co., 1966, Chap. 3, "Implications for Practice," p. 24.

Jensen, Deborah M. *Ward Administration*. St. Louis: C. V. Mosby Co., 1952, "Characteristics of a Good Assignment," p. 88.

——. *Nursing Service Administration*. St. Louis: C. V. Mosby Co., 1962, Chap. 24, "Patient Care Depends on Adequate Time Coverage."

Lambertsen, Eleanor. *Education for Nursing Leadership*. Philadelphia: J. B. Lippincott Co., 1958, Chap. V.

The trouble with life is that it's so daily.

Quadriplegic Dilemma

Leroy was injured in an automobile accident when he was 16 years old. He suffered a broken back, which left him with paralysis of both legs and partial paralysis of both arms. Leroy came from a wealthy home. Although he was used to having the things money could buy, he was essentially well disciplined up to the point of his accident. Following the accident his family placed him in a private hospital near their home.

After recovery from the acute conditions of the accident, Leroy was advised that the best place for his rehabilitation was the state hospital. Here all facilities he would need were available. At first the family objected to placing Leroy in a state institution, but after a visit to the hospital they agreed that it was the best place for their son. They objected again, however, when advised to place Leroy in a ward with other paraplegics. When the doctor explained the psychologic value of being with others who had similar problems, his parents finally consented.

In his new environment Leroy had a difficult time adjusting emotionally. He had been used to private nurses, and when he made requests that had formerly been granted, he was now told that he was making unreasonable demands on the nurses' time. He disliked being cared for by licensed practical nurses or by student nurses. He soon became so frustrated that he flew into a rage, hammering his elbows until they were sore and shouting insults at everyone who came near him.

Once this behavior pattern was established, Leroy repeated it every time he felt he was not getting enough attention. Although the resident physician threatened all sorts of punishment, none was ever given. Things became so difficult that a registered nurse and two licensed practical nurses asked to be transferred to other departments or threatened that they would quit. The result of Leroy's behavior was that most of the workers on his ward avoided him as much as possible. This resulted in minimal care for him. Before long Leroy developed a decubitus ulcer on his left heel. He had not been turned in bed enough.

By this time Leroy had become especially vocal and complained that he was being discriminated against. The doctors could not understand what was keeping Leroy in such a constant state of aggravation. To satisfy the nursing staff they moved Leroy to another floor and into a private room. This also seemed agreeable to Leroy and to his family. His mother was assured that Leroy would get adequate care. But Leroy soon missed his companions on the ward. To obtain more attention from his nurses he resorted to rubbing his arms on the sheets until his elbows were red, then demanding immediate care for them.

One of the nurses overheard Leroy's mother telling him he was not getting good nursing care. "The only way you'll get good care is to keep complaining," she advised him. So with the encouragement of his ill-informed mother, Leroy continued to be an irritable, uncooperative patient. Leroy's doctor finally advised his mother that it would be best not to visit her son until his emotional problems were better adjusted. She promptly received permission from the chief of the medical staff, Dr. Findley, to visit her son.

Leroy began to tell his mother exaggerated stories about how badly he was persecuted. He claimed that nobody liked him, that aside from minimal nursing care, no one ever came near him, and that in physical therapy they enjoyed making him suffer by forcing him to exercise beyond his physical ability. Following these complaints, his mother consulted the state attorney general, who had been a friend of the family for many years. "Since all people caring for Leroy are state employees, can't you insist that they give my boy better care?" she begged.

The next morning Dr. Findley called a meeting of all persons who cared for Leroy in any way. This included doctors, residents, nurses, the psychologist, the social worker, physical and occupational therapists, aides, and orderlies. "Something has got to be done about Leroy!" he began. "The state attorney general will have all our heads in a basket! Has anyone the least idea why Leroy acts the way he does?"

"He's a spoiled brat," said one.

"He'll be satisfied with nothing less than full-time, private-duty nursing care," offered another.

"Would his family pay for it?" asked another.

"How many of you really like Leroy?" asked Dr. Findley. Complete silence followed.

"Who has tried to talk with him since this trouble began?" Again complete silence.

"Why don't you like him?" At this all answers came eagerly and at once.

"He doesn't appreciate our care."

"He complains, no matter how we treat him."

"I tried being nice to him, and he just growled back at me."

"He's very hostile and often profane."

"He demands too much attention."

Dr. Findley held up his hand for silence. "Why does he demand attention? Because he doesn't feel he's getting enough."

"Does he have any real friends here? Are there any patients with whom he is friendly?" asked the psychologist, Dr. Farr. Everyone shook his head "No" to these questions.

"What do you know about him? Does he like to play cards? What does he do for recreation? What was he like before he was injured?" asked Dr. Findley. Again silence.

Dr. Findley was getting impatient, "Well, what are we going to do about it?"

"Perhaps we should all make an effort to be friendly, no matter how he reacts," said Dr. Farr.

"Let's all try to find out more about him as a person."

"If he enjoyed swimming, perhaps he could work off some energy in the pool," suggested the occupational therapist. "Let's keep him too busy to think for a while and see if he calms down."

"Let's give him the 'Cupcake Treatment,' " [1] said one of the nurses cheerfully. "Each day one of us will try to do something especially nice for him."

"Three cheers for the attorney general," shouted a resident and everybody laughed.

"We've got to be subtle," said Dr. Findley. "If Leroy gets the idea we're pampering him due to pressure from above, it won't help him or our situation. Try to understand him sincerely. Try to realize what his frustrations are and work around them. We'll meet again next week to see how we are doing with Leroy. Have you any further suggestions, Dr. Farr?"

"Not at this point," said Dr. Farr. "I think we're on the right track."

Questions

1. What could the hospital administration have done to help Leroy before the attorney general entered the situation?

2. What could any of the people have done to reverse Leroy's behavior?

3. Was Leroy justified in his behavior?

4. What should the head nurse on his ward have done in advising those under her supervision?

5. Are there any indications of negligence or legal lack of due care in this case?

References

Bird, Brian. "The Nurse Is the Patient's Interpreter," *The Modern Hospital*, 84: 51–54, 1955.

[1] "Cupcake Treatment" is a term used by Esther Lucile Brown in *Newer Dimensions of Patient Care*, Part II (New York: Russell Sage Foundation, 1962), pp. 161–63.

————. *Talking with Patients*. Philadelphia: J. B. Lippincott Co., 1955.

Creighton, Helen. *Law Every Nurse Should Know*. Philadelphia: W. B. Saunders Co., 1962, Chap. VII.

Hershey, Nathan. "Hospitals' Expanding Responsibility," *American Journal of Nursing*, 66: 1546–47, 1966.

Lesnik, Milton J., and Bernice E. Anderson. *Nursing Practice and the Law*, 2nd ed. Philadelphia: J. B. Lippincott Co., 1955, Chap. VII.

Perrodin, Cecelia M. *Supervision of Nursing Service Personnel*. New York: The Macmillan Co., 1954.

Raths, Louis E., and Anna P. Burrell. *Do's and Don'ts of the Needs Theory*. Bronxville, New York: Modern Education Service, 1951.

If I can stop one heart from breaking,
I shall not live in vain.
If I can ease one life the aching,
Or cool one pain,
Or help one fainting robin
Unto his nest again,
I shall not live in vain.

Emily Dickinson [1]

[1] Edited by Martin Dickinson Bianchi and Alfred Leete Hampson (Boston: Little, Brown & Co., 1945. Original poem copyrighted 1890.)

Neophyte's First Day

Marie Gilman had dreamed of being a nurse from the earliest memories she had. She played nurse with her dolls, and as she matured, she pictured herself helping others through their trials of pain and illness. She conscientiously studied all her college courses, prerequisite to her hospital experience.

She realized she must understand human behavior in order to meet the emotional needs of patients whose problems were often generated in or intensified by illness. She probed her own self-awareness as a basis for understanding others. She studied ways to know the patient, who he was, and how he saw himself and ways of finding out what his prehospitalization world was like.

She trembled with anticipation on her first day in uniform as a student nurse. Anxiously yet timidly she hurried to her assigned ward. There she heard morning report and received her case load for the morning. As a new student Miss Gilman had only a few patients. Mr. Bartholomew was recovering from a simple appendectomy and was to be discharged in a matter of days. There were no complications, but the head nurse noted that he still preferred to walk bent over rather than straight.

Her second patient was an elderly lady who had sustained a fractured hip many weeks before. Mrs. Brown's progress was slow since her old bones did not heal quickly. Her lengthy hospital stay made her increasingly concerned over her financial affairs.

Since the third patient, Mrs. Wright, was scheduled for surgery before noon, Miss Gilman was to care for her for just half a day. Mrs. Wright was a diabetic in her late thirties, who had developed an ulceration on her left ankle that would not heal. Instead, it enlarged and grew worse, and the tissue around it began to die. Under the circumstances the doctors decided that an amputation below the knee would be necessary. They had discussed the surgery with Mrs. Wright but she was far from accepting her situation. The young student felt great sympathy for this patient. How hard it would be to face the problems of caring for a home and raising a family when she returned from the hospital. "I must try to comfort her," Miss Gilman thought.

She hurried through the morning routine with Mr. Bartholomew and Mrs. Brown as quickly as possible in order to devote most of her time to Mrs. Wright. She put in a call for her instructor to help her with the preoperative procedures, which were all new to her. Her mind raced wildly with what she would say, what words would be most assuring.

At last she was at Mrs. Wright's bedside. She assisted with her bath, listening attentively to her patient as she did so. She recalled lectures on such situations and tried her best to give sound, encouraging answers, the right answers. She felt she was doing a pretty good job, for Mrs. Wright was beginning to relax and sound a little more optimistic. Miss Gilman could think of nothing else but this patient and the wonderful feeling of her accomplishment. She was totally unprepared to see the orderly stroll in.

"Mrs. Wright? We're ready to take you downstairs," he said.

"But it can't be so soon," the student cried in an amazed tone.

"She was on call and the operating room is ready." The orderly was trying to remain calm. He could see there was going to be a waiting period for him. "Besides, it's almost 11."

Miss Gilman flew to the desk where she was able to intercept one of the nurses. "Has my instructor come to the floor?"

"No, did you call her again to make sure she was coming and knew what time to be here?"

"No, I was very busy."

"Well, I'll have to get the head nurse. She'll be able to get you some help. I'm very busy right now."

Soon the head nurse returned, looking rather disgruntled at having been interrupted. The student was growing more embarrassed as time passed, and the orderly tapped his fingers impatiently. Even Mrs. Wright began to feel upset since she did not understand the delay.

Because there was no instructor on the floor, the head nurse administered the preoperative medications, prepared the patient, and completed her chart. When Mrs. Wright was finally on her way downstairs, the head nurse turned to Miss Gilman. "And just why wasn't that patient ready for the O.R.?" she asked. "You have plenty of time and your assignment wasn't too busy. If the first instructor you called was busy, you should have tried another. Instead, you delayed the orderly and the surgeons, took me away from my patient, and caused Mrs. Wright great anxiety."

The sharp words of the head nurse stung Miss Gilman. There were no words of "Well done" for what she had done with her other patients or any congratulations for her handling of Mrs. Wright's emotional problem. There were only reprimands.

That evening, Miss Gilman returned to her dormitory a disheartened, disillusioned girl. She had given good physical care to her patients, of that she was sure. And she had called upon all her knowledge and personal strength to give Mrs. Wright the emotional support she needed. Where had she failed? True, she should have been more specific with her instructor, but was the little delay in medications and procedure more important than the comfort she had given? At the end of her first working day on the floor, the student found herself confused about her duties and even about her role as a nurse.

Questions

1. Was Marie Gilman's supervision adequate?

2. Were the aims of nursing education fulfilled?

3. Was she treated in any way as a co-worker, rather than a student?

4. Where was her supervisor?

5. Who should have counseled her concerning her first day as a nurse?

References

Davis, Fred (ed.). *The Nursing Profession.* New York: John Wiley and Sons, Inc., 1966, Chap. 3, "The Organizational Context of Nursing Practice," p. 109.

Famularo, J. S. *Supervisors in Action.* New York: McGraw-Hill Book Co., Inc., 1961.

Henderson, Virginia. *The Nature of Nursing.* New York: The Macmillan Co., 1966, Chap. 3, "Implication for Practice," pp. 24–31.

Jensen, Deborah M. *Ward Administration.* St. Louis: C. V. Mosby Co., 1952. The characteristics of a good assignment are listed on p. 88.

Lambertsen, Eleanor C. *Education for Nursing Leadership.* Philadelphia: J. B. Lippincott Co., 1958, Chap. VII, "Aim of Professional Education."

Lockerly, Florence. *Communication for Nurses.* St. Louis: C. V. Mosby Co., 1958. Criterion of objectivity and maturity are discussed on pp. 23–29.

Morrison, Luella J., and Mary A. Farris. *Approaches for Coworkers in Professional Nursing.* St. Louis: C. V. Mosby Co., 1962, Unit III, "Advancing with the Nursing Profession."

Perrodin, Cecelia M. *Supervision of Nursing Service Personnel.* New York: The Macmillan Co., 1954.

Rogers, Martha E. *Educational Revolution in Nursing.* New York: The Macmillan Co., 1961, Chap. IV.

Seidenfeld, M. A. *Psychological Aspects of Medical Care.* American Lecture Series, Publication No. 44. Springfield, Illinois: Charles C Thomas, 1949.

Lord, fill my mouth with worthwhile stuff
and close it when I've said enough.

If You Can Keep Your Head . . .

The Hathaway Memorial Rehabilitation Center was in the midst of major reconstruction, which consisted of adding several floors and air-conditioning the entire building. During all this hubbub the medical staff and patients accepted the discomfort and inconvenience as they looked ahead to better days. In general the entire staff could pride themselves on their patience and an ability to work as a team under such conditions.

During this period the patients were housed in an adjoining building and had to be transported daily to the center for treatment, being trundled back and forth on litters or in wheelchairs. To facilitate scheduling under these circumstances the physical therapists often found themselves directing and supervising the aides for this transportation service. Under normal conditions the aides took orders from and were responsible to the nursing staff. Friction began to occur. The aides resented the additional work involved in such transportation between buildings and were not used to taking orders from the physical therapists. They grumbled as they waited for the situation to return to normal, when their responsibility would be only that of transporting patients from their rooms to the various departments of the center without an outdoor struggle, often through rain or snow. These undercurrents were mild and usually the patients arrived for their treatment on time.

Working in this situation was a 38-year-old therapist named Ted. Although mature in years, Ted was new to the profession of physical therapy. This was his first year in the profession of his choice, which came after many years of employment that had been consistent only in its inconsistency. His childhood was one of poverty and hardship. His early life did not escape the influence of "gangs," and he dropped out of high school after completing his second year. Eventually he served nine years in the Navy, saw active combat at Pearl Harbor, and completed his high-school education. Immediately he enrolled for his physical-therapy education and became a qualified physical therapist.

When the center inquired at the university for references, they were told that this "diamond" was very rough. His academic work was high, but his language was crude. He was often rude and outspoken. He had shown marked and progressive improvement, but still needed guidance in order to overcome his handicap.

One morning Ted found that his patient was late and went to the adjoining building to see what was causing the delay. He found that the patient was ready in his wheelchair surrounded by several aides who were seemingly unconcerned about transporting the patients on time. He did not directly ask any of the aides to assist him. He did make it obvious that he was angry by talking loudly to the patient about the aides' unwillingness to be prompt in the transfers. Gladys, one of the aides in the group, spoke up, "It's none of your business what I does. I does what I want in my own sweet time!"

Ted responded, "You b——! It's about time you did what you were assigned to do. Furthermore, who in the h—— do you think you are, talking to me that way?" Ted pushed the patient over to the department where he mentioned to his supervisor that he had had some difficulty with an aide but did not go into detail.

Early that afternoon Gladys appeared in the department where Ted was working. He was treating a young girl whose mother was standing by observing the treatment. Student physical therapists were also present. Gladys renewed the argument, making a face at him and saying, "Man, who gives you the right to tells me what to do?"

Furiously Ted turned on her. Pointing his finger in her face, he said, "I do what I'm supposed to do. It's about time you do what you are supposed to. Anyway, what the h—— are you doing here?"

Gladys replied, "Don't you strike me, you physical therapy b——!"

Ted, losing complete control, shouted, "I wouldn't hit you, you b——, but you're lucky I wouldn't because if I did I'd hit you so hard your a—— would make a hole in this concrete floor!"

Gladys ran crying to her immediate employer, the supervising nurse. All the nurse could find out from Gladys was that Ted had threatened to strike her. The nurse phoned Ted's supervisor and asked how a therapist of that caliber could remain on the staff. "A professional who would stoop so low as to swear and physically threaten the aides should be fired," she said. "Don't you know how hard it is to keep aides?"

Several patients also reported the incident, remarking how disgraceful they thought the scene had been. Some patients became so upset that sedatives had to be given, and mothers decided that such surroundings were uncouth and made arrangements to transfer their children to other hospitals. One of these parents was considering giving a grant of several thousand dollars to the center. Students were stunned. Along with everyone else, Ted was miserable too.

The administrator of the center stormed into the department demanding that the therapist be fired. The supervising physical therapist found no time to act that day (perhaps deliberately) because he wanted to gain a little time. Ted had been a good therapist and, until now, had tried hard to fit himself into this completely new class of society.

Early the next morning the administrator, having cooled off a bit, called to say that Ted should not be fired on his recommendation alone. He assured the therapist that he would back whatever decision he made. As the supervising therapist put the phone back on its hook, he wondered how he was going to handle this situation.

Questions

1. Which principles of administration have been violated?
   a. by the chief administrator
   b. by the chief physical therapist
   c. by the supervising nurse
   d. by the orderlies
   e. by Ted

2. Was there unity of command? Who should have controlled the orderlies?

3. What would have brought about more effective supervision?
   a. of the orderlies
   b. of the physical therapists

4. What type of administration would be best for this situation? How would you change it?

5. Put yourself in the place of:
   a. the aide
   b. the supervising nurse
   c. the chief physical therapist
   d. the hospital administrator
   e. Ted

6. What policies could be initiated to prevent such friction?

References

Crow, Alice, and Lester D. Crow. *Understanding Interrelations in Nursing.* New York: The Macmillan Co., 1961.

Dooher, Joseph M. (ed.). *Effective Communication on the Job.* New York: American Management Association, 1956.

Forsdale, Louis. "Helping Students Observe Processes of Communication," *Teachers College Record,* 67(Nov.): 120, 1965.

Frank, L. K. "Interprofessional Communication," *American Journal of Public Health,* **51:** 1798, 1961.

Freedman, Milton. "Effective Group Relations," *Physical Therapy Review,* **36:** 231–33, 1956.

Geitgey, Doris A. *A Handbook for Head Nurses.* Philadelphia: F. A. Davis Co., 1962, Chap. 8, "How to Exchange Information With Others."

McMurry, Robert N. "Clear Communications for Chief Executives," *Harvard Business Review,* **43:** 131, 1965.

National Industrial Conference Board. *Studies in Personnel Policy, No. 129: Communicating with Employees.* New York: National Industrial Conference Board, Inc. (n.d.), p. 40.

FIGURE 2. (From Rebecca McCann. *Complete Cheerful Cherub*. New York: Crown Publishers, Inc., 1932, p. 45.)

WHEN POMPOUS PEOPLE SQUELCH ME
WITH THEIR REGAL ATTRIBUTES
IT CHEERS ME TO IMAGINE
HOW THEY'D LOOK IN
BATHING SUITS

Rose O'Neill, *Kewpies: Complete Calendar Girl*,
New York: Crown Publishers, Inc., 1913, p. 38.

Frustrations of Being a Student

Jane came from a normal, happy home. Her father was a lawyer and her mother active in the civic affairs of their small community. There were five children in the family, of whom Jane was the second oldest. She was used to assuming responsibility and did so with readiness and skill. She was an excellent student, active in many campus organizations, and she had never been severely criticized at home or at school.

One Saturday Jane hurried back to the university to keep an appointment she had requested with the director of her school of occupational therapy. To say she was upset would put it mildly. She felt, during this first three weeks of her clinical education, that the entire venture was bound to end in failure.

The department in which she was affiliated was one of the best for variety of patients and research into new techniques and equipment and was extremely well organized. However, it lacked flexibility and was autocratically administered by a vociferous, outspoken, and strong-minded individual who often corrected staff members or students in front of each other or in front of patients. Jane's immediate supervisor reflected this policy of the departmental administrator by using frequent and frank criticism, regardless of who might be present, often showing emotion that students interpreted as impatience or disgust.

The incident that sent Jane back to her school for help began when she spoke to her supervisor, calling her by her first name at a departmental picnic. This brought a tirade of criticism. The criticism was that her relationships with the patients were poor;

the patients had no confidence in her; she lacked warmth and understanding. A final piece of advice was offered to her: if she could not learn to disguise her high degree of academic knowledge and learn to talk on the same level with the patients, they would never be able to understand what she was trying to teach them.

Questions

1. What changes could the departmental administrator make in her own behavior that would help this department?

2. If the student was wrong to address her supervisor by her first name, was the picnic the place to discuss her other weaknesses?

3. What could the director of the school do concerning:
   a. the administrator of the department
   b. the supervisor
   c. the student.

References

American Management Association. *Effective Communication on the Job, A Guide to Employee Communication for Supervisors and Executives.* New York: American Management Association, 1956.

Broderick, Thomas J. "How to Help Supervisors Evaluate Employees," *The Modern Hospital,* 95: 89–93, 1960.

Brown, Milon. *Conference Leaders' Guide to Effective Supervision.* New York: The Macmillan Co., 1956.

Etzioni, Amitai. *Modern Organizations.* Englewood Cliffs, New Jersey: Prentice-Hall, Inc., 1964, Chap. 4, "From Human Relations to the Structuralists," pp. 32–48.

Take it to someone else's department! I don't want it in mine!

Try to Buck a Policy

A group of young hospital employees were discussing the hospital food at lunch one day. They mentioned how bored they were with the usual cafeteria food. This led to a discussion of their favorite foods and the conclusion that they all liked lasagna.

Joan, a student of medical technology, offered to bring lasagna for the group on Thursday. "We can cook it in the ceramic kiln in occupational therapy. They won't be using it at noon."

On Thursday Joan arrived with her lasagna prepared. The department head of occupational therapy laughed at the idea and heated the kiln. Soon the delightful aroma of lasagna floated through the department. Dr. Cumberland, chief of physical medicine, followed his nose to the kiln. "What's going on here?" he asked.

"We're cooking lasagna in the kiln. Would you care to join us?" said Joan.

"Get that out of here and now!" said Dr. Cumberland. "We can't have this department smelling like a cafeteria. What will everybody think? Do you want Mother Superior on our necks? Take it somewhere else to cook it. There's a kitchen on the next floor up."

Joan went up to ask if their oven could be used.

"We don't have an oven," said the nurse. "Try one of the wards. They have ovens to prepare special menus for the patients."

Joan went to ward B's kitchen and asked a nurse if it would be all right to cook the lasagna there.

"I'm sorry," hedged the nurse. " I haven't the authority to say 'yes' or 'no.' You'll have to ask Miss Conway, the head nurse."

Upon finding Miss Conway, Joan asked again if the oven could be used to cook the lasagna.

"You'll have to get permission from Mrs. Manning. I wouldn't dare give you permission myself. If she smelled it, she'd immediately want to know what was going on. I don't think she would like it."

Steadfastly Joan sought Mrs. Manning, the supervisor, who immediately remonstrated, "If I allow one of the staff to use the ward kitchens, everyone would be cooking his own lunch in a week. The kitchens are only for the preparation of food for patients. Why don't you ask the main cafeteria if they will let you finish cooking it, just this one time."

Joan telephoned the main cafeteria. Miss Kukevitch, the dietitian, exclaimed, "Any food that gets cooked down here gets sold across the counter. We can't get into the habit of letting employees cook their own food. Who would buy meals from the cafeteria if we let everybody cook his own lunch? What a ridiculous idea!" She banged down the phone.

By the time Joan returned to the occupational therapy department the lasagna was done. Her cohorts had opened the windows and turned on the fan. Since it was past noon and Dr. Cumberland had gone to lunch, they quickly gathered and ate the lasagna. Like stolen fruit, it tasted very good. However, they firmly resolved not to try such a stunt again.

Questions

1. Who could have advised Joan against cooking lasagna in the hospital?

2. What was the obvious administrative philosophy in this hospital?

3. From the standpoint of human relations what better choice of words could have been used by:

a. Dr. Cumberland
b. the nurse who referred Joan to Miss Conway
c. Miss Conway
d. Mrs. Manning
e. Miss Kukevitch?

References

Bellows, R. M. *Psychology of Personnel in Business and Industry.* New York: Prentice-Hall, Inc., 1955.

Burling, Temple, Lentz, Edith M., and Wilson, Robert N. *The Give and Take in Hospitals. A Study of Human Organization in Hospitals.* New York: G. P. Putnam's Sons, 1956.

Freedman, Milton. "Effective Group Relations," *Physical Therapy Review,* **36**: 236–39, 1956.

Jensen, Deborah M. (ed.). *Nursing Service Administration.* St. Louis: C. V. Mosby Co., 1962.

Larrabee, Eric. "Who Gets the Message?" *Vogue,* **137**: 165, 1961.

Lingren, Henry C. *The Art of Human Relations.* New York: Hermitage House, Inc., 1953.

Monaco, Anthony. "Our Biggest Hurdle Was Tradition," *The Modern Hospital,* **95**: 98–99, 1960.

Rossell, Eve. "Human Relations Principles Are the Hospital's Principle Problem," *The Modern Hospital,* **80**: 62–64, 1953.

FIGURE 3. (From Rebecca McCann. *Complete Cheerful Cherub*. New York: Crown Publishers, Inc., 1932, p. 130.)

Mrs. Sherwood Gets Ideas

Mrs. Darby, R.N., looked up from the report she was writing to see Mrs. Sherwood approaching her desk. She noticed how pale the patient looked and was getting to her feet as Mrs. Sherwood mumbled, "I feel like I'm going to faint." Before Mrs. Darby could reach her, the patient crumpled to the floor. Mrs. Darby called to another nurse to phone for Mrs. Sherwood's doctor and continued to move toward the patient, who was beginning to revive as Mrs. Darby reached her side.

Mrs. Sherwood attempted to rise but Mrs. Darby cautioned, "Easy, Mrs. Sherwood; your doctor has been called and will be here in a few moments."

"I'm all right now," said Mrs. Sherwood.

Other nurses arrived with a pillow and a blanket which Mrs. Sherwood rejected saying, "My goodness, such a fuss! I'm perfectly all right now. Let me get up and go back to my room."

Mrs. Darby recalled that Mrs. Sherwood was hospitalized for studies related to diagnosis for low blood pressure. "Just lie still and wait for Dr. Green," she instructed. "He'll be right along."

"But I feel so foolish lying here on the *floor!*" exclaimed Mrs. Sherwood, attempting once again to get up.

"Did you hurt yourself when you fell?" asked Mrs. Darby as she gently restrained Mrs. Sherwood's efforts to rise.

Mrs. Sherwood reflected as she moved her arms and legs experimentally. "No, not at all. May I get up now?"

Dr. Green arrived and took charge. He questioned Mrs. Sherwood and examined her briefly. After he checked her blood pressure, he allowed her to walk back to her room, but he left orders with Mrs. Darby that Mrs. Sherwood should remain in bed until he gave further orders.

"Was Mrs. Sherwood injured in any way by her fall?" asked Mrs. Darby.

"I checked her carefully and found no injury," replied Dr. Green.

Mrs. Darby spent the next few minutes recording all these events in an unusual-incident report before going on with her usual duties.

Three days later Mrs. Sherwood complained to Dr. Green that her back was giving her a great deal of pain and that her neck was very stiff. She moved cautiously as if afraid the next move might cause more pain. Dr. Green could find no real muscle spasm and also noted absence of tenderness in the areas usually painful with such symptoms. Leaving Mrs. Sherwood's room he asked Mrs. Darby if she had filed an accident report concerning Mrs. Sherwood's fall. Mrs. Darby showed him a copy of the report she had written, explaining, "I didn't consider it an accident because no one was hurt. I did fill out an unusual-incident report." It read as follows:

> At 10:25 A.M. on Thursday, Oct. 10, 1963, Mrs. Sherwood came toward the office, saying she felt faint. As I went toward her, she slumped to the floor. Dr. Green was called and arrived at 10:30 A.M. After examination Dr. Green stated the patient was not injured by the fall in any way. She returned to bed, with orders to stay there until further order from Dr. Green.
>
> Mrs. George Darby, R.N.
> Head Nurse, 5th Floor

"That's good!" said Dr. Green. "I believe Mrs. Sherwood is getting ideas about suing the hospital for some vague injuries. Keep a copy of that report with Mrs. Sherwood's chart. We may need it in court."

The next day Mrs. Sherwood's lawyer, Mr. Bond, asked for an

appointment with the hospital administrator, Mr. Edwards. Mr. Bond advised Mr. Edwards of Mrs. Sherwood's intention to sue. Excusing himself for a few minutes, Mr. Edwards went to the fifth floor, talked briefly with Mrs. Darby and looked at the report, called Dr. Green, and then returned to his office.

"Mr. Bond," he said with assurance, "you had better advise Mrs. Sherwood that if she files suit she will have to pay all court costs if she loses. It will cost her at least $500 for your fee and court charges, and her chances for winning are about as good as a camel crawling through a needle's eye! I have medical proof and qualified witnesses to testify that she was not hurt by her fall. I also have her own words claiming she was not hurt. In front of at least five witnesses Mrs. Sherwood answered Mrs. Darby's question, 'Did you hurt yourself when you fell?' with, 'No, not at all. May I get up now?' Now, Mr. Bond, have you any other questions?"

"No," replied Mr. Bond. "I believe I will advise my client as you suggested."

Mrs. Sherwood experienced immediate relief from her painful symptoms and was discharged without further complication within a few days.

Questions

1. Why is it important to file unusual-incident reports?

2. Without a written report would Mrs. Sherwood's chances of winning the case have been much better?

3. What additional procedure would have protected the hospital legally?

4. Why did Mr. Bond agree so readily with Mr. Edwards?

References

Baltz, F. L. "Need for Medical Records," *Hospital Management,* **91**(March): 6, 1961.

Barrett, Jean. *The Head Nurse.* New York: Appleton-Century-Crofts, 1962, pp. 38, 41.

Blum, Richard H. "Good Organization Means Fewer Law Suits," *The Modern Hospital,* 91: 59–62, 1958.

Creighton, Helen. *Law Every Nurse Should Know.* Philadelphia: W. B. Saunders Co., 1962, Chap. IV.

Geitgey, Doris A. *A Handbook for Head Nurses.* Philadelphia: F. A. Davis Co., 1962.

Hershey, Nathan. "Hospitals Expanding Responsibility," *American Journal of Nursing,* 66: 1546–47, 1966.

Horty, John F. "Courts Set the Pattern for Medical Records," *The Modern Hospital,* 100: 142, 1963.

Kelly, Cordelia W. *Dimensions of Professional Nursing.* New York: The Macmillan Co., 1962, Sect. V, "Legal Rights and Responsibilities."

Lesnik, Milton J., and Bernice E. Anderson. *Nursing Practice and the Law,* 2nd ed. Philadelphia: J. B. Lippincott Co., 1955, pp. 234–304.

Owen, Joseph K. (ed.). *Modern Concepts of Hospital Administration.* Philadelphia: W. B. Saunders Co., 1962, Chap. 9, "The Hospital Insurance Program."

When you feel dog tired at night, it may be because you growled all day.

Who Should Supervise the Supervisor?

These incidents took place in a hospital for chronic diseases. The patient capacity was 600 beds, of which only 375 beds were filled because the hospital was understaffed. The majority of patients were on a charity basis and had to be residents of the state.

The administrative atmosphere was one of unrest. Although there was an organization chart that indicated clear lines of communication, each department existed as though it was the only one in the hospital. The hospital administrator was so busy with public relations and top administrative duties that he seldom concerned himself with any of the departments unless a crisis was brought to his attention. The medical staff communicated well with all departments, seldom interfering with interdepartmental administrative problems.

The rehabilitation department included occupational therapy, speech and hearing, and physical therapy. The doctor in charge was permissive, giving as well as receiving suggestions as he concentrated most of his attention on the many patients who were referred to his department. He left the administrative duties to each of the departmental directors.

The supervisor of the occupational-therapy department was autocratic to the point of demanding personal favors. Mrs. Byron was tactless, demanding, selfish, and otherwise lacking in those intangibles that would command respect. However, she was intelligent, knew the mechanics of the department well, and was professionally aware of her duties. Her entire problem was one of personality. Professionally and academically she was sufficiently capable. She had been supervisor for three years and now nobody listened to her or obeyed unless he had to.

Under the doctors the atmosphere of the department was democratic, but under the supervisor the atmosphere was autocratic. Thus, staff members were forced to change their attitude to fit the person. If both the doctor and the supervisor were present, one mentally tossed a coin. The doctors, the supervisor, and the staff were all well aware of their problems. The atmosphere often got so charged that tempers flared—usually behind the back of the one concerned.

The hospital administrator rarely visited the department and aside from requesting an annual report was seldom involved in the internal conflicts of the department.

A constant chain of aggravating events kept everyone's nerves on edge. Mrs. Byron averaged about three and a half full days of work per week, but never marked the time off for herself. Being the supervisor she was responsible for recording her own hours. On the other hand, if a staff member walked in five minutes late it would be noted, and the paycheck was cut accordingly. Mrs. Byron was expecting a baby and many members of her family were sick. Between these two factors she was constantly taking full days off with no loss of vacation time or pay. This not only made the other therapists jealous, but made extra work for the senior therapists. They resented this since they were not getting paid to carry out the supervisor's duties. When new therapists or students came on the staff, she would ask them to run personal errands for her. "Get my shoes for me in the lounge, please," was not an unusual order.

At one staff meeting Mrs. Byron discussed what to do with "the student" in front of everyone, including the student. She claimed that when she assigned the student a patient the student asked her to review the technique for her. Mrs. Byron felt that the student should have learned her techniques well enough during the academic aspects of her education to make review unnecessary. Therefore, she refused to review the material.

As she watched the patient being treated by the student, she asked the student to step aside and finished the treatment herself. This embarrassed the student, who felt that this patient would have no confidence in her ability to treat him for the rest of his stay in the hospital. "The student" also wondered what she would be called if there were more than one student at the meeting—"the tall student," "the blue-eyed student," "the stupid student."

One day Mrs. Byron stormed into the lounge shouting, "Damn it all anyway! Where is my newspaper?" She hesitated when she saw the nameless "student" sitting, then continued to bluster, "Oh, there it is! I wish people wouldn't take it. Just look at it! It's all botched up!" With this she grabbed the paper and stomped out. One therapist had borrowed the paper because it was lying on the table in the lounge, and the student had helped "botch it up."

The staff held grudges against Mrs. Byron for months. They consoled themselves by discussing mistakes she had made since she first started working there. The memory of the staff for insignificant, petty details was truly amazing. Not only did they talk, but they actively rebelled whenever the situation became unbearable. An example of this occurred when Mrs. Byron forgot to assign someone to clean and lock up the department. The staff refused to do it. They walked out, leaving the department in a mess: soiled linens, scattered equipment, and all the lights on. It was mentioned that the medical director would be furious, but they claimed they did not care. They were sick of taking over Mrs. Byron's responsibilities during her constant absences.

Every day brought more friction. The corrosion of the atmosphere did not seem to affect the treatment the patients were receiving. Only the more perceptive patients were aware that this situation existed. All concerned had the ethical sense to preserve the atmosphere around the patients. Because Mrs. Byron was out so much, she did not have much time to cause trouble. Fortunately she would be leaving soon, and another woman who was very well liked would be taking her place. The staff counted the days and mentally gritted their teeth while waiting for her to leave.

Questions

1. If you were the administrator would you have relieved Mrs. Byron of her responsibilities rather than waiting for the time she chose to leave?

2. If so, what reasons would you give her for demotion or dismissal?

3. Would the departure of Mrs. Byron "straighten out the problems existing in this department?

4. List the ways in which the staff contributed to the departmental problems rather than helped.

References

Bash, Wendell H., and F. K. Berrien. *Human Relations—Comments and Cases.* New York: Harper and Brothers, 1957.

Brown, Milon. *Conference Leaders' Guide to Effective Supervision.* New York: The Macmillan Co., 1956.

Burling, Temple, Lentz, Edith M., and Wilson, Robert N. *The Give and Take in Hospitals—A Study of Human Organization in Hospitals.* New York: G. P. Putnam's Sons, 1956.

Cooper, Alfred M. *How to Supervise People,* 3rd ed. New York: McGraw-Hill Book Co., Inc., 1957.

Etzioni, Amitai. *Modern Organizations.* New Jersey: Prentice-Hall, Inc., 1964, Chap. 4, "From Human Relations to the Structuralists," p. 32.

Lawshe, C. H., and Nagle, Bryant F. "Productivity and Attitude

Toward Supervisor," *Journal of Applied Psychology,* 37: 159–62, 1953.

Masur, Jack. "Top Brass Should Follow the Golden Rule," *The Modern Hospital,* 95: 79–83, 1960.

It is difficult to see a fly on the tip of one's nose.

Thirty-Five Steps to Treatment

Sturbridge Clinic was a large, 1000-bed hospital and research center. It was a chosen spot for interns, residents, and students in any of the medical specialties for it had established an excellent reputation in all medical fields. Sturbridge especially excelled in neurosurgery and orthopedics. One could easily get lost searching for its main entrance since it spread over acres of land on the fringe of a large city. The parking lot that was used by most patients was three blocks from the main entrance.

Dr. Morris, a resident in the physical-medicine department, noticed one day that many of his outpatients seemed very hot and tired before their treatment began. Being new to the hospital, he could not understand why. He asked Dr. Scott, the medical director of the department, about it. Dr. Scott said he had not noticed this because he seldom saw the patients exercising. He examined the patients and prescribed their treatment and the therapists took over. The two doctors went into the clinic to observe some of the patients' activities. By talking with the therapist they found that Mr. Cole, a paraplegic, always appeared hot and was invariably late. Mr. Cole was always accompanied by his wife, who was overly attentive and distracted him from concentrating on his treatment. Dr. Morris asked him if he could not become more independent of his wife. Mr. Cole looked surprised, saying hotly, "I couldn't even get to this department without her to help me up that miserable flight of stairs! If you think that's easy, you take a pair of crutches and try it!"

Dr. Norris and Dr. Scott decided it would be wise to investigate the entrance for clinic patients. They were amazed to find that there was indeed a long flight of stairs involved. They looked at all entrances to their building in search of a better one. The emergency-room entrance was on the level of the street, but no cars were allowed to drive in unless an emergency patient was involved. They consulted the outpatients' clinic, which shared the same floor with them. The nurse in charge stated that she had noticed the same problem and that all outpatients probably came in through the main entrance. This problem was then presented to the hospital administrator.

The administrator assigned Mr. Frolich, a resident in hospital administration, to take one week to study the situation thoroughly and offer suggestions. He promised Dr. Scott that some action would be taken. Mr. Frolich decided to observe and to keep a record of the patients who used the main entrance's long flight of stairs. In one day he was appalled at the number of people who struggled up and down the entrance with every sort of neurologic or orthopedic condition. People with braces, casts, and crutches staggered along with the help of friends and relatives. Old people with heart conditions stopped halfway up to catch their breath. One man, who, Mr. Frolich later found, had had brain surgery, weaved about clutching the railing as his worried wife and sister assisted him up the stairs.

Mr. Frolich's report read,

> There is a definite problem concerning the stairs at the main entrance. More than half the patients can barely struggle up the steps into the hospital. I suggest that all patients be allowed to use the ground-floor entrance to the emergency room.

Dr. Northby, who was in charge of the emergency room, was notified that this had been advised. He immediately objected, saying, "we can't have a whole parade of patients crowding our parking lot and entrance. How will we know our emergency patients from others if everyone is walking through the emergency room!"

Mr. Frolich suggested that they give each patient who should avoid stairs a special pass. This would be shown to the guard at the entrance to the parking lot; the patient would be let out at the emergency entrance, and the driver would take the car to the parking lot three blocks away. Dr. Northby still objected saying that he could not be responsible for these patients as they arrived and had to go through his department. Mr. Frolich then suggested that orderlies meet each patient to assist him as needed and to see that he got to the right department. Dr. Northby felt that this would only add to the unwanted people in his department, but finally agreed to this arrangement—only until a better plan could be worked out.

After the departments were informed of the new arrangement, Mr. Frolich continued his study of the problem. He took another day to observe the main entrance. To his surprise all sorts of handicapped people still struggled up or down the steps. When he asked them why they did not obtain passes to enter through the emergency room, they all looked surprised and claimed no one had told them they could.

Mr. Frolich was afraid to offer his next suggestion, but taking the bull by the horns, he went to his supervisor and said, "What this hospital needs is a new main entrance. Why anyone ever planned one with so many stairs, I'll never know, but this problem won't really be solved until the stairs just don't exist. What's more, there should be a parking lot for patients so they don't have to hike three blocks. If that's impossible, we should at least have a place for cars to drive up to a street-level door."

Mr. Frolich's suggestions were presented to the board of directors. After a brief study by the finance committee the following recommendations were made:

> The finance committee feels that since this hospital has the reputation of being one of the finest in the

country, it cannot allow this serious problem to continue. It is, therefore, our first priority among the expenditure of funds to construct a ground-level main entrance with a place for cars to drive up to the door. No place can now be seen for a parking lot nearer the hospital, but if the land directly across the street ever becomes available a parking garage is recommended.

Dr. Northby read these recommendations with a sigh of relief, and Mr. Frolich was pleased that his suggestions had been listened to.

Questions

1. How long would this situation have existed if Dr. Norris had not noticed the tired patients and brought it to someone's attention?

2. Why had no one thought of it before?

3. Could Mr. Frolich's suggestions be improved upon?

4. Was Dr. Northby right to be uncooperative? How could he have been more helpful?

References

"Administrative Resident Learns by Listening" (editorial), *The Modern Hospital*, 98: 95, 1962.

Armstrong, R. W. "Empathy," *Nursing Times,* 52: 1006–9, 1956.

Howard, S. Kenneth, and F. C. LeRocker. "What Decisions Do Trustees Actually Make?" *The Modern Hospital*, 94: 83, 1960.

Jackson, Laura G. *Hospital and Community.* New York: The Macmillan Co., 1964, Chap. 1, "Interdependence of Doctor and Hospital," and Chap. 9, "Buildings and Builders."

Komaiko, J. K. "The Fine Art of Listening," *Parents Magazine*, 36: 40–41, 1961.

"Traffic Flow Keeps Patients Out of the Public Eye" (editorial), *The Modern Hospital*, 95: 115–18, 1960.

Experience: a wonderful thing that enables you to recognize a mistake when you make it again.

The Dean's Breakfast Was Late!

Suzan was a student medical technician in a general hospital affiliated with her school. The first patient she was assigned happened to be the dean of the school of nursing from her own state university. Suzan was to give her a basal metabolism test. Although Suzan was very apprehensive as she approached her patient, her supervisor assured Suzan that she would be right outside the door if anything went wrong or if she had any questions. Carefully Suzan explained the equipment, which she knew the dean was familiar with, and then she asked, "Did you sleep well last night?"

The dean replied with some apprehension, "No, I did not! At five o'clock two orderlies had a loud argument just outside my door, and I haven't slept since."

Concerned, Suzan excused herself to consult with her supervisor, who told her to proceed. Suzan applied her equipment to the patient and began her test. Before long she noticed her patient's face was getting very red, and upon checking the recording, she found it to be extremely erratic. She removed the mask immediately and, trying not to show anxiety, took the recording out to her supervisor. Soon she returned to explain to the dean that she was very sorry, but there had been no oxygen in the tank. She would return soon with the oxygen. This was at 10 A.M.

As Suzan stepped into the elevator, she dropped the valve from the oxygen tank into the elevator shaft through the space between the floor and the elevator. She went to the nearest phone and called Mr. Bailey in the maintenance department. Mr. Bailey explained to her that this involved turning off the power for all elevators while he climbed to the bottom of the shaft to find the valve. He advised Suzan to wait where she was until he brought it to her, saying it might take 15 or 20 minutes.

Almost immediately the hospital administrator, Mr. Peabody, began getting anxious phone calls. The x-ray department complained they were falling behind in their schedule because for some reason the patients were not there for their appointments. The operating room called with the same problem. Surgeons were scrubbed and waiting for their patients, but the patients were not there. The physical-therapy department called several floors to ask why the patients were not there for their treatments.

No one realized that the problem was that no elevators were running. No one had been informed that the power would be off. At the end of 30 minutes the besieged Mr. Peabody had pinpointed the trouble and informed all departments that elevator service would resume as soon as possible. As Suzan watched the confusion, she sincerely hoped no one knew it was her fault.

It was 11 o'clock when Suzan returned to the dean, who asked somewhat impatiently where she had been and complained that she could not have breakfast until this test was over. Suzan's next problem was attaching the new oxygen tank to the basal metabolism equipment. She soon realized she did not know how to do this. She left the room to find her supervisor no longer there, but found an intern to help her. When the equipment was finally in working order, the test was given, but the results were worthless owing to the patient's agitation.

At 11:30 the dean was greeted by a cheerful nurse who said, "Now you can have your breakfast," as she placed the tray before her. The dean stared at a cold poached egg and limp toast and decided to wait for lunch.

Questions

1. What policy could the administrator establish with the maintenance department to facilitate quick notification to all departments of any power failure?

2. In the face of emergency how could the administrator quickly notify all departments?

3. Was Suzan's supervision adequate?

4. How could any of the existing problems have been minimized?

References

Averill, Lawrence, and Florence Kempf. *Psychology Applied to Nursing.* Philadelphia: W. B. Saunders Co., 1951.

Brown, Amy Frances. "Organization of Clinical Learning Experiences," *Nursing Outlook,* 5: 97, 1957.

Cooper, Alfred M. *How to Supervise People,* 3rd ed. New York: McGraw-Hill Book Co., Inc., 1952.

Larrabee, E. "Who Gets the Message?" *Vogue,* 137: 165, 1961.

Redfield, Charles E. *Communication in Management.* Chicago: University of Chicago Press, 1954.

Viguers, Richard T. "What It Takes to Be a Good Supervisor," *The Modern Hospital,* 91: 63–66, 1958.

———. "Building a Hospital Communications Network," *Hospitals,* 36: 48–51, 1962.

You can't make a silk purse out of a sow's ear.

The Stingy Board of Directors

Green Acres Home and Hospital for the Chronically Ill and Aged was privately owned. The philosophy of the board of directors was, "Good medical care, with reasonable cost to the patient, keeping overhead expenses as minimal as possible to assure an annual profit." The hospital administrator was an agreeable fellow who tried to reflect the philosophy of the board to the employees. He struggled with a minimal budget for services and supplies. Because salaries were low there was a rapid turnover of workers, especially in the lower salary ranges such as kitchen help, orderlies, and janitors. Because of this, orderly service was often poor. Patients were often late for appointments, which upset the schedules of all departments.

Many of the patients were hemiplegics, paraplegics, and amputees who needed a great deal of nursing care. Each section of the hospital was staffed by a head nurse. These head nurses were all registered nurses. Working with them were licensed practical nurses, student nurses and nurses' aides, orderlies, and cleaning personnel.

Green Acres offered an accredited course for licensed practical nurses. This provided them with student nurses who were of great assistance at no cost except their board, room, and education, most of which was inservice training. There were six foreign resident physicians who needed one year of supervised experience before they could become licensed in America. These doctors provided full-time medical coverage of the hospital. They were under the supervision of the chief of the medical staff. Because they came from six different countries, there was a language barrier between the residents and with other hospital personnel and patients. Since the chief of medical staff was not with them at all times, many of the residents' orders were misunderstood and sometimes incorrect.

Ambulation was ordered by one resident for an 80-year-old woman recovering from a fractured hip. He did not order physical therapy but asked two student nurses to help the patient walk. While doing this the patient fell, breaking the other hip. The family sued for $125,000 because, they claimed, this meant the woman would never walk again.

One patient who was incontinent owing to a broken back complained to his doctor that he had to wait two hours for a nurse to clean him and his bed following uncontrolled elimination. The patient claimed this lack of care caused the bedsores he was developing over his sacrum.

The physical-therapy department was minimally staffed but could provide half-hour treatments for each patient under normal conditions. However, if a therapist was sick, his appointments were cancelled and the patients went without treatment that day. One day three therapists were out sick and so many appointments were cancelled that the patients all complained to their doctors who, in turn, brought their total complaints to the attention of the chief of the medical staff. The chief of the medical staff called the department head in physical therapy insisting that all patients be treated. When told this was impossible, he became angry, saying, "I don't care what you do! Shorten everyone's treatment, but treat every patient, even if you can't give them good treatment."

Under these conditions the residents complained they were not treated with proper respect and that the hospital employees doubted them and questioned their orders. The nurses and other employees working with them claimed they were overworked and underpaid. Everyone became cross and impatient. Finally, patients and their families claimed the care was poor and this led the doctors to call for a meeting of the board of directors, demanding that something be done to improve the situation.

Questions

1. What needed to be done to improve the situation at Green Acres?

2. Was the philosophy of the board of directors ethically and morally sound?

3. What could any of the employees do to improve the situation?

4. If you were a board member what would you do?

References

George, Gordon. "Doctor-Patient Relationships," *America,* **90**: 12–16, 1953.

Howard, S. Kenneth, and F. C. LeRocker. "What Decisions Do Trustees Actually Make?" *The Modern Hospital,* **94**(April): 93, 1960.

Owen, Joseph K. (ed.). *Modern Concepts of Hospital Administration.* Philadelphia: W. B. Saunders Co., 1962, Chap. 7, "Financial Management."

Rozos, E. John. *Leadership on the Job. Guides to Good Supervision.* New York: American Management Association, 1954.

———. "Everybody Should Have a Part in the Budget," *The Modern Hospital,* **91**: 87–90, 1958.

FIGURE 4. (A Salo *Laughing Matter* cartoon. New York: Chicago Tribune–New York News Syndicate, Inc., 1963.)

General Pomeroy—The Autocrat

Stonybrook Veterans' Home and Hospital was located in a rural setting. It offered general medical and surgical care for veterans of the armed forces. Most of the patients could be classified as chronically ill, although temporary and acute disabilities were often treated. All patients had to be financially unable to pay for private hospital care.

The administrative atmosphere was military and autocratic. The commandant, General Pomeroy, held firm control over all policies concerned with the domiciliary home and the civilian medical staff. He insisted his orders be followed to the letter and often visited the department to make sure his orders were being carried out. Although there were three assistant administrators, General Pomeroy often issued notices or gave orders directly to employees without consulting any of his assistants. Under these circumstances the following incidents took place.

A general order from the administrator was sent to all patients, employees, and departments that read:

> There will be no smoking by anyone, patients or employees, except in the following designated areas: day rooms, dining rooms, offices, washrooms, bedrooms. If a patient is confined to bed, a capable person must be with him while he is smoking.

The pathology department held a meeting of all its staff to discuss this memo and to decide where they could smoke. They could not smoke in their washroom because flammable supplies were stored there. They decided instead to designate the hallway as a smoking area. It contained a fire extinguisher and was always supervised by orderlies. A memo to General Pomeroy stated:

> Since the pathology department stores flammables in its washrooms, it has designated the hallway just outside the pathology department as its smoking area. This is near the fire extinguishers and will be supervised by orderlies.

It was signed by Dr. Whitley, pathologist. An immediate and brief reply from General Pomeroy read:

> There will be no exceptions to the first copy of smoking rules. If this rule is violated, strict disciplinary action will be taken.

Six weeks later fire broke out in the washroom of the pathology department. Someone telephoned to report the rapidly spreading fire and pulled the fire emergency lever. Patients and employees escaped from the department and hurried to close the fire doors and all possible doors to patients' rooms. The fire extinguisher in the hall was of little use. The flames spread so rapidly that people found themselves trapped on that floor. Because of the hospital's rural location it was some time before fire equipment arrived. In the meantime patients and employees followed procedures they had learned during frequent fire drills. They knew by the flashing light over the firebox where the fire was located. Patients and employees were evacuated as quickly as possible from all uninvolved areas. On the floor where the fire had started no patients could be evacuated through the hallway. Those patients whose doors were closed were not injured except for some degree of smoke poisoning. Those whose rooms were not protected were injured, and five patients died from burns.

All employees on this floor stayed and tried to help patients escape through windows when firemen's ladders were outside. All patients and employees on the floor above remained where they were until notified by firemen that they could safely escape by the south exit. When the fire was finally under control, a human chain of firemen, employees, and ambulatory patients handed along all people unable to walk.

One patient on the ninth floor, who had not walked for three months, got up and ran out of the building. Another old man slept through the whole thing. All patients who could be were discharged to their homes. One man who had surgery for a ruptured vertebral disc that same day was discharged to his wife who was a nurse. A patient with implanted radium to be removed at a certain time was located and the radium removed. General Pomeroy was, on the whole, pleased with the discipline with which patients and employees responded to the emergency. The general remarked that it was a good thing that everyone was used to following orders. Discipline paid off when such emergencies arose. He located Dr. Whitley and discharged him on the spot for not removing the flammable objects from a designated smoking area.

Questions

1. What could General Pomeroy or Dr. Whitley have done to prevent the fire?

2. What attitudes toward General Pomeroy prompted personnel to deliberately create a dangerous situation by smoking near the flammable material?

3. Ultimately who was responsible for the fire?

4. Who would be legally liable for the injuries and deaths?

5. Who would be morally responsible for the injuries and deaths?

References

Boettcher, Ernest M. "How to Make a 'Fire-Safe' Hospital Safer," *The Modern Hospital,* **101:** 83, 1963.

Cooper, Alfred M. *How to Supervise People,* 3rd ed. New York: McGraw-Hill Book Co., Inc., 1952.

Dimock, M. E. *The Executive in Action.* New York: Harper and Brothers, 1945.

McGrath, Robert. "To Fight Fire—First Conquer Fear," *The Modern Hospital,* 85: 58–61, 1955.

McMurry, Robert N. "Democracy Is What We Strive for, But Autocracy Gets Things Done," *The Modern Hospital,* 90 (April): 52, 1958.

Owen, Joseph K. (ed.). *Modern Concepts of Hospital Administration.* Philadelphia: W. B. Saunders Co., 1962, p. 76.

Simon, Herbert A. *Administrative Behavior.* New York: The Macmillan Co., 1959.

Soltonstall, Robert. *Human Relations in Administration.* New York: McGraw-Hill Book Co., Inc., 1959.

The only good part about losing your head is that you are the last one to miss it!

The Case of the Neglected Patient

Miss Harvey, administrator of the physical-therapy department in a small general hospital, was working under rather difficult conditions. Within a week she would enter the hospital for surgery for the removal of a tumor which was possibly malignant. It seemed best, however, for her to keep working rather than to stay at home thinking about it. Since she would necessarily be unable to work for some time after the surgery, she was anxious to keep working to earn all the money possible before the operation.

About 2:30 P.M. the orderly brought Mrs. James to the physical-therapy department for diathermy and massage to the low back. Her pain was idiopathic. All x-rays were negative and there was no history of illness or injury, yet Mrs. James complained of severe and lasting pain over the past six weeks of such extent that she was unable to sleep. Miss Harvey made the patient as comfortable as possible and applied diathermy to the low back as prescribed. She then continued with other duties about the department. She neglected to set a time clock, feeling certain she would remember to come back to her patient in time.

At 3:00 P.M. Miss Harvey's personal surgeon came to the department looking very concerned. He explained that the biopsies looked as if there was indeed malignancy and asked her to come with him immediately for further biopsies. They left the physical-therapy department in some haste, leaving a nonaccredited, foreign-trained therapist and the orderly to complete the day's work. At closing time the usual check of the department, which was the responsibility of the chief therapist, was not carried out. Usually all equipment was checked to be sure it was disconnected, and all booths were opened to be sure that every patient had left.

At dinner time Mrs. James was not in her bed, nor could she be found any place on the ward. The police were notified, and the bureau of missing persons put out the alert. They assumed she would be wandering the streets in a hospital bathrobe since her clothing was still in her room.

At 7:00 P.M. Mrs. James awoke from the first comfortable sleep she had experienced in six weeks. She found herself in the darkened room, still under the diathermy machine. She managed to crawl out from under the machine, find her slippers and bathrobe in the dark, and feel her way toward the door. She was somewhat amazed to find that the door was securely locked from the outside with no way for her to open it. She then checked to see if there were other exits such as windows or doors leading to a fire escape. There were none.

Being a calm person by nature she did not pound on the door and scream, but sat down to think for a moment. She remembered that, just before she went to sleep, she overheard the conversation between Miss Harvey and her doctor and felt sorry for her. Therefore, she decided not to telephone her because she already had enough trouble. She looked up the phone number of the nonaccredited therapist, Miss Hilke, and dialed her number. An alert hospital telephone operator, who was aware of the missing patient, noticed the light on her switchboard and immediately notified the night nurse in charge. The night nurse went to the physical-therapy department, unlocked the door, and assisted the patient back to her room.

Doctors examined Mrs. James for possible burns or other injuries that might have developed from four hours of diathermy. Mrs. James claimed her pain was absolutely gone and that she had not felt so well for six weeks. Lawyers were consulted concerning the possibility of suit, but Mrs. James (still feeling sorry for the therapist) claimed she was cured, not injured, and quickly signed legal releases that she had no intent to sue.

Questions

1. There are several instances of legal irregularities in this story. List them and discuss them.

2. There are several incidences of ethical irregularities. List and discuss them.

3. What would have been the consequences if the patient chose to sue?

4. What would have been the right thing for Miss Harvey to do?

5. What would have been the right thing for the hospital to do?

References

Blum, Richard H. "Good Organization Means Fewer Law Suits," *The Modern Hospital*, 91: 59–62, 1958.

Creighton, Helen. "Law for Physical Therapists," *Physical Therapy Review*, 38: 22–25, 1958.

Hershey, Nathan. "Hospitals Expanding Responsibility," *American Journal of Nursing*, 66: 1546–47, 1966.

FIGURE 5. (From Charles M. Martin. "Eight Ways to Get Along with Doctors," *The Modern Hospital*, No. 6[Dec.], 1960, p. 63.)

How Not to Solve a Problem!

Mr. Gorke was a young resident administrator at Harpers Community Hospital. He was conscientious and anxious to prove himself as a hospital administrator. Mr. Dooly, hospital administrator and supervisor of the residents, believed in letting the residents "learn by doing." He answered their questions and assisted them whenever they asked for help but never gave them specific instructions. If confusion resulted he would then be as helpful as possible, explaining better ways in which a problem could have been resolved.

Harpers Community Hospital could accommodate 500 patients. It was a teaching center for residents in several medical specialties. Mr. Dooly assigned the following problem to Mr. Gorke. Dr. Montague, chief of medical service, reported that excessive loitering of the nonprofessional help in the self-service elevators frequently made patients late for the operating room. The problem reached a climax when a woman was forced to deliver her baby in the elevator. Mr. Gorke ordered guards for the four self-operated elevators. These elevators had green doors and were referred to as the "green" elevators. He then sent the following memo to all hospital departments:

> Beginning next Monday morning only persons transporting patients or equipment will be allowed on the green elevators between the hours of 8 A.M. and 3:30 P.M. All other personnel will use the blue elevators.

Mr. Gorke's first phone call relating to this situation was from the dietitian, who explained, "Mr. Gorke, for the past 30 years food has been transported on special small elevators that are neither green nor blue. Do you still insist that we use the blue elevators?" Mr. Gorke apologized and explained that he did not know about these elevators. He told the dietitian to continue to use the special elevators.

Meanwhile, the guards were conscientiously insisting that doctors, nurses, aides, and all other people not transporting patients or equipment use the blue elevators. One bewildered aide tried to insist that the green elevators were the only ones near her department. "I'm on my way to pick up a patient in x-ray," she explained. "If I have to take the blue elevator I'll have to walk through the intensive-care unit to the west wing, go down to the second floor, bring the patient back on the green elevator, and return to the fourth floor via the intensive-care unit!"

The guard listened sympathetically and then said, "I'm only following orders, you'll have to talk it over with your supervisor."

The aide went to her supervisor with her complaints. "I'll be spending most of the day hiking through the intensive-care unit! All my patients will be late. Can't you call the hospital administrator and straighten this out?"

The supervisor called Mr. Dooly and explained their problem. "I'm sorry," said Mr. Dooly, "but this is not my problem, you'll have to contact Mr. Gorke." She called Mr. Gorke's office. His secretary explained that he was on the second floor trying to settle a dispute about the new ruling concerning the use of the green elevators. The supervisor explained her problem, and the secretary promised to have Mr. Gorke call back or visit her as soon as possible.

On the second floor Mr. Gorke listened while the nurse in charge of the outpatient service explained that normally the blue elevators would be all right for them to use. However, because of construction between the blue elevators and the outpatient clinic there was no way for patients to reach their department

without crawling through the construction. Mr. Gorke gave instructions to the guards on the elevators to allow anyone going
to the outpatient clinic to use the green elevators.

When he returned to his office, his secretary told him about
the problem on the fourth floor. He went to the supervising
nurse, who explained the aide's plight. Mr. Gorke then instructed
the guards to allow fourth-floor personnel to use the green elevators.

When Dr. Montague came to work and tried to use the green
elevators, he staunchly announced to the guard that he most certainly would not hike around to the blue elevators. The green
ones would take him directly to surgery and he demanded ad-
mittance to the elevator. The guard stood his ground, blocking
entrance to the elevator, repeating politely, "I'm only following
orders, sir." Furious, Dr. Montague stormed into Mr. Dooly's
office. "What in the world is going on around here?" he shouted.
Mr. Dooly once again said, "I'm sorry, Dr. Montague, it isn't my
problem. You'll have to see Mr. Gorke."

"Who, may I ask, is Mr. Gorke?"

"He's our new resident administrator. You can find him in his
office, just two doors down the hall."

Mr. Gorke returned from the fourth floor to find Dr. Montague pacing up and down in his office. "See here, young man,
who do you think you are, asking busy doctors to waste their
time running from wing to wing to use the blue elevators? Why
did you make such a silly ruling?"

Mr. Gorke tried to explain the problem of the nonprofessional
help loitering in the elevators. "That is one reason your patients
were late in getting to surgery," he continued, hoping to
strengthen his point.

Dr. Montague, however, was in no mood to lose his argument.
"Do you think doctors are loitering on the elevators? They
haven't the time to loiter. Now you come along with me and tell
that guard to let me use the green elevators. I'm already a half
hour late and the whole day's schedule is ruined. You're upsetting the whole routine of this hospital!" Mr. Gorke went with

him to the elevator where he told the guard to let all physicians use the elevator. Discouraged and demoralized, Mr. Gorke went to Mr. Dooly for advice.

Questions

1. What advice could Mr. Dooly give?

2. What communication problem existed at Harpers Community Hospital?

3. Was Mr. Gorke's learning experience worth the frustration it caused the hospital?

4. Would another method of supervision have prevented upsetting the entire hospital?

References

Chamberlain, Neil. *Management in Motion.* New Haven, Conneticut: Labor and Management Center, Yale University, 1950.

Dooher, Joseph M. (ed.). *Effective Communication on the Job.* New York: American Management Association, 1956.

Martin, Charles M. "Eight Ways to Get Along with Doctors," *The Modern Hospital,* **95:** 63–64, 1960.

National Industrial Conference Board. *Studies in Personnel Policy, No. 129: Communication with Employees.* New York: National Industrial Conference Board, Inc. (n.d.), p. 40.

Radler, Leonard. "A Manager's Job Is to Help Employees Grow," *The Modern Hospital,* **95:** 119, 1960.

A camel is a horse put together by a committee.

A Committee Tries to Function

Harlow General Hospital was a large hospital located in the heart of a busy city. It often had many emergency cases that needed immediate admission. Dr. Wilson, chief of medical staff, became concerned when there seemed to be increasing difficulty finding beds and rooms for these emergency patients. At his next staff meeting he asked all doctors to discharge any patients who could be sent home and asked if they knew why this problem seemed worse than usual at this time.

"Tenth floor is closed due to a lack of nursing staff," volunteered one doctor.

"That's been so for over a year now, so it shouldn't be the cause of our immediate problem," replied another.

"We have a lot of patients who might be discharged to rest homes for minimal recovery care," was still another suggestion.

"Why don't we appoint a committee to study all patients who have been here longer than two weeks?"

"That's a good idea, Dr. Peters," said Dr. Wilson. "Will you be chairman of such a committee and select two other doctors to help you?"

There was general laughter over the fellow who suggested work being assigned the responsibilities. Dr. Peters was, however, eager to do it and quickly asked Dr. Fritz from medicine and Dr. Buntz from orthopedics, who agreed to help. Dr. Peters was a neurosurgeon. They began their investigation as soon after the meeting as they could and decided to take one floor of the hospital each day, checking all patients who had been there more than two weeks. They began on the third floor, which was the first floor with beds, and agreed to work their way upward daily.

Their first problem was Mrs. Martin, who had entered the hospital five weeks earlier with a fractured left ankle as a result of a fall on the ice outside her apartment. She was 63 years old and the mother of five married children, three of whom lived near her. Her doctor set her ankle and put a cast on. After a couple of days she was referred to physical therapy for instructions on using crutches with no weight on the left leg. Mrs. Martin was fitted with crutches and treatment began twice a day as requested. Within the next week she was able to manage quite well on the crutches and even on the stairs. However, she did not want to go to the home of any of her children, nor did she want to go to a rest home for a few weeks. Her children suggested the rest home, and at once she developed a pain in the "good" leg. Her doctor decided to have her stay a little longer until she was more confident and could return to the apartment in which she lived alone.

Although the therapist felt she was ready to be discharged, her doctor felt a few more days could be permitted. A walker was put on the bottom of the cast, and Mrs. Martin was able to put weight on the left leg. For her this was a step that would require many days of training, although most people learned in one day. It was decided that she stay two more days. The next day Mrs. Martin complained of a painful heel in the cast. Any pressure, such as walking, was unbearable. The leg was checked, but nothing was found. In the middle of the next week her doctor left for a ten-day vacation. The patient was still there and now was walking without crutches or a cane. Orders were left that the patient should stay until her doctor returned. This patient was still reporting twice a day to physical therapy, although she was able to walk without assistance during the day. Not only was she taking up the time of the therapist (time that should have been spent with patients who needed more help), but also she demanded the time of the nurses and occupied a bed, both of which were needed by others in serious conditions.

Dr. Buntz contacted Mrs. Martin's doctor by long-distance telephone and received permission for her discharge from the hospital to her own home.

As the three doctors continued their study of patients' charts, they found that several of the charts were missing. They asked the nurse in charge where these charts were.

"Who knows?" she replied. "We send them along with the patients to x-ray and occupational therapy and the social worker needs them. If they aren't in any of those places, some aide or orderly is probably carrying them about for half a day."

Dr. Peters called Dr. Wilson, stating, "Our study of these patients is being seriously delayed because the charts are not here. Can't we ask to have the charts left on the floor?"

"I see no reason why we can't," replied Dr. Wilson. "Give us until tomorrow morning to get all the charts back, and I'll call the supervisor of nursing services to be sure all nurses know that the charts are to stay on the floor."

The next day the committee was able to continue checking patients like Mrs. Martin. They were encouraged by the cooperation of all the other doctors, who quickly agreed to discharge patients whom the committee recommended. They discovered that Mr. Jones had been waiting a month in the hospital for his artificial leg. He was being charged $25 per day for a semiprivate room. He was going to physical therapy once daily for exercise. Upon examining him, they found he knew his exercises well, and the muscles of his hip seemed in excellent condition. He knew how to apply his own bandage and demonstrated that he could do this well. A check with his doctor confirmed that this patient could care for himself at home. The patient cheerfully agreed to be discharged to his home and family. Similarly, Mrs. Berry had been waiting six weeks for a brace to be delivered but was very efficient with her own care.

The committee began to wonder why it took so long to get

braces and artificial limbs. Dr. Peters called the companies concerned and from both of them he received the same information.
They had previously received orders directly from the physician,
billed the patient directly, and were therefore able to provide
prompt delivery. Recently they had been informed that all orders must be placed through the hospital purchasing department. This involved numerous forms and much red tape. Often
they did not get the order for two or three weeks after it had
been placed. Dr. Peters questioned Mr. Smith, the purchasing
agent, about these delays. Mr. Smith explained, "Formerly, artificial legs and braces were ordered by the patient, according to
the doctor's prescription. The patient was billed directly by the
company and often became confused upon receiving two bills,
one from the hospital and one from an outside company. Sometimes the wrong piece of equipment was delivered to the patient
because we had no central record of the order. For such reasons
we decided that all braces and artificial limbs must be ordered
through the purchasing department. Before this procedure was
established we had no record of the transaction. Now the patient
receives one bill, and we pay the brace maker. It is really a
much more businesslike process."

"But think of the additional cost to the patient as he waits
here in the hospital for three or four weeks!" reminded Dr.
Peters.

"I'll see if I can speed up the process," promised Mr. Smith.
"Could we discharge them until such equipment comes, then re-
enter them?"

"Not all of them," said Dr. Peters. "Some of them need continued treatment for other reasons. You try to get through the red
tape faster, and we'll discharge all those we can. Okay?"

"Okay," agreed Mr. Smith.

Most of the patients were anxious to leave. One old man
grumbled that he did not want to be a burden to his children,
but agreed to leave although he still needed some bedside care.
Arrangements were made with the public health nursing association for this care.

On the third morning Dr. Peters overheard a nurse saying into the phone, "I'm sorry, no charts can leave the floor. . . . I can't help that, our orders are that no charts are to leave the floor. . . . Well then, send the patient back!" As she slammed down the phone, Dr. Peters asked what the trouble was.

"Dr. Rhodes, in physical medicine, says he can't adequately evaluate the patients without their charts; so they are not able to treat them. He's also pretty mad because no one told him about the new regulation. He's been getting the same story from every floor, and he doesn't know where the order came from. I think he's on his way to see the hospital administrator."

Dr. Peters quickly called Dr. Wilson, who said he would go to the administrator's office right away. When Dr. Wilson entered Mr. Ashford's office, he found Dr. Rhodes, of physical medicine, accompanied by several other people from other departments. Everyone was talking at once, but all were saying the same thing. "We can't give the patient due care unless we have access to his chart." "We can't run all over the hospital every time we need to read a chart." "Who gave such a stupid order in the first place?" "With the elevator service in this hospital we'd spend all day trying to get to the floors to read the charts!"

Mr. Ashford held up both hands, begging for silence, and when he had their attention he said, "I'm sorry, no such information came across my desk. I'll have to find out about it and let you know what we can do."

Dr. Wilson spoke up, "I gave the order. A committee is trying to evaluate all patients who have been here more than two weeks and they need the charts."

"And what are we supposed to do in the meantime?" asked Dr. Rhodes. "This cripples our department completely. How long will it take this committee to finish their evaluation?"

"Two or three weeks," said Dr. Wilson. "We'll have to work something out."

"Can we have a meeting between all the departments who need charts and the committee?" suggested someone. "Perhaps we could find a way to solve our problem."

"That would involve a lot of people," replied Dr. Wilson. "How about letting the chart go, but asking an aide to return it immediately without waiting until the patient is treated?"

Everyone present agreed that this sounded like a good thing to try. The committee and nursing service were notified. The committee work went forward with a minimum of friction from this point on.

Questions

1. What communication problems existed or were created by Dr. Wilson?

2. Was the committee the best solution to the total problem?

3. What policies could have been established to prevent further overcrowding?

4. At what point should Mr. Ashford have been included in the plans?

References

Agnes, Edith A. "How Can Nurses Serve Two Masters?" *The Modern Hospital,* 97: 111–13, 1961.

Brown, Esther Lucile. *Newer Dimensions of Patient Care,* Part 2. New York: Russell Sage Foundation, 1962, pp. 65–68, "The Competing Chain of Command."

Davis, Harry A. "Let One Person Do All the Purchasing," *The Modern Hospital,* 101: 14, 1963.

McMurry, Robert. "Clear Communication for Chief Executives," *Harvard Business Review,* 90: 131–47, 1965.

Martin, Charles M. "Eight Ways to Get Along with Doctors," *The Modern Hospital,* 95: 63–66, 1960.

Owen, Joseph K. (ed.). *Modern Concepts of Hospital Administration*. Philadelphia: W. B. Saunders Co., 1962, Chap. 15, "Organizing the Medical Staff."

Sigmond, Robert M. "What Utilization Committees Taught Us," *The Modern Hospital*, **100**: 67–71, 1963, "Who's the Short Stay Surgeon? Me!"

FIGURE 6. (A Charles Schulz *Peanuts* cartoon. California: United Feature Syndicate, 1955.)

No Matter How Hard We Try . . .

Meeting Street School offered a comprehensive and integrated outpatient program of habilitation or rehabilitation for infants, preschool children, and children up to 16 with a variety of disabilities. The majority of these children had some form of cerebral dysfunction. The school was also a research center where any new approaches to treatment were incorporated, with funds available to send any of its employees to study new methods as they were being developed. A statewide, rotating board of directors governed the operation and policies of the school, counseled by a medical advisory committee and a professional consultant board. The medical director worked closely with all patients and was available full time should any of the specialists wish to consult him. The philosophy of the school was: "Pride and respect for each other as an essential for the integration of the therapies, with four-way communication going upward or downward and to either side, as rapidly as necessary to facilitate the best possible patient care."

The school was financed by a state society of a national organization. It had sound personnel policies, including four-week vacations, accident and health insurance, and salaries in line with accepted regional scales. All employees were fully accredited, and they regarded each other as professional equals. A public education program was conducted through newspapers, reprints, speakers, and television to instruct the community concerning the importance of rehabilitation at an early age.

Unlike many institutions which have a speech and hearing department in one section, an occupational-therapy department in another section, and a physical-therapy department in still another, this school integrated these three major therapies into classes where they worked together as a team. This enabled the children to receive well-rounded and integrated therapy. It also enabled the therapists to observe the "whole child" and to participate in the entire rehabilitation program. In addition to this group approach the program included individual appointments, medical clinics, and home visits.

The school was also a research center where any new approaches to treatment were incorporated.

The school functioned under the following basic policies:

1. The earlier in the life of the child the rehabilitation team sees the child, the better the future development and prognosis.

2. The school was set up on a day-care, outpatient basis because it was felt the child's place was at home.

3. This plan strengthened parental attitudes by making them feel a definite part of the program.

4. Each child received medical and therapeutic treatment. The therapies followed the child's interests, contributing to the normal pattern of growth and development.

5. In the team approach the therapists considered the child as a whole. Their purpose was to rehabilitate him to find his place in the world physically, socially, emotionally, and mentally within the limits of his disability.

6. A total medical diagnostic study needed to be made on each child as a base line before any treatment program could be started. Psychologic studies and social work were incorporated into the initial diagnostic study.

The school's atmosphere was one of permissiveness and closeness. The executive director felt that staff members would func-

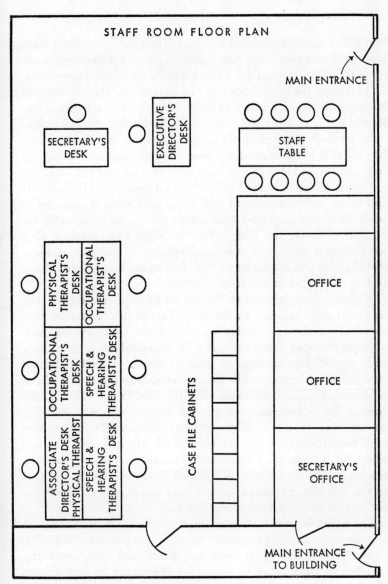

FIGURE 7. *Staff room floor plan.*

tion better through physical nearness. Therefore, the offices were combined into one large staff room. Because the desks were arranged without regard for each person's specialty, communication between the disciplines was at a maximum. Therapists could integrate and interrelate ideas. (See Fig. 7.) The executive director did not have a private office but followed through her philosophy by having a desk in the large staff room so that she might be available to the staff at any time. This arrangement facilitated communication between the executive director and the staff.

The administrative atmosphere was cooperative. All therapists and other people associated with the school were encouraged to voice their problems and opinions to the executive director for discussion among the staff. When decisions were reached, they were carried through. Conflicts of opinion or mistakes in judgment could, and did, arise in this democratic atmosphere. Some of them occurred in the following ways.

A patient was referred to the school by a private doctor. She was seen and evaluated by the team. Part of this evaluation consisted of psychologic testing by one of the staff psychologists. This psychologist was a man who liked everything to be orderly and proper. His findings on this particular patient indicated cerebral dysfunction with mental retardation and emotional problems. From a conference with the mother, he felt that she was an intelligent, but very anxious woman who was probably contributing to the child's emotional difficulty by demanding high performance of this retarded child. He included all these things in his report. A confidential summary letter of the staff findings was then written by the staff medical director and sent to the referring physician. Such letters were marked "Confidential" across the page in large red letters.

The following week the woman returned to the school for an appointment. She was no sooner seated in the psychologist's office than she pulled a letter from her purse and indignantly demanded to know what he meant by the things he had written about her child and herself. It was the confidential letter written to her doctor! The psychologist was completely taken by surprise. His first impulse was to tell her that she had no right to have the letter, which was written in confidence to a doctor. He was about to ask her to give him the letter when he stopped himself, realizing that this would in no way help the situation. Instead he sat back in his chair and calmly assured her that the very reason for her appointment was to discuss and clarify her child's condition and to improve it if possible. He asked how she had obtained possession of the letter. She told him that she was a nurse; so her doctor had seen fit to give it to her. The remainder of the session went fairly smoothly.

The psychologist reported the incident to the staff medical director, who in turn wrote to the referring physician politely, requesting that all future letters be kept in strict confidence.

One day as the staff sat together eating their lunch they planned a party for the following Saturday night. On the next Monday in the office a physical therapist made a comment to the executive director about the party. Before the executive director could answer, the social worker interrupted with, "What party Saturday night?" An embarrassing silence followed. The social worker had not been with them at lunch when the party was planned and had not been invited. They realized they had also not included the teacher, who worked on a part-time basis. The executive director was the first to recover her tongue. "I'm so sorry," she said. "We planned it at lunch and I guess you weren't with us at the time."

The social worker turned to the therapist, saying angrily, "You're the party kid around here. How come you didn't tell me about it?"

"It was just an oversight," said the therapist. "I simply didn't realize that you didn't know about it."

The social worker talked about missing the party for the rest of the day. Everyone secretly vowed to be very certain that everyone knew about the next social event.

One of the research projects concerned a study on children who had undergone a complete transfusion at birth because of the RH factor to see if there were any signs of minor neurologic damage. These children were evaluated by each member of the team at two-year intervals. One week before such a re-evaluation was to take place the associate director heard via the grapevine that the part-time teacher would not be there for part of the evaluation. She decided not to do or say anything until she heard directly from the teacher. Two days before the study the teacher announced that she could not be there for the first day of the study. She showed a physical therapist how to administer part of the tests. She said nothing about the rest of the testing. The second day the teacher was there for part of the day, then left, again asking others to do her testing. This behavior continued throughout the study, and consequently, data on six patients could not be located. The research would not be valid without these records. The executive director did not become aware of the teacher's absences until the records were missed. At that time she asked the teacher to be present at all evaluation and to do her own testing.

Each new referral was subjected to the series of tests by the team of therapists. These cases, whether they were actively in a program at the school or whether they were referred elsewhere, were supposed to be re-evaluated at six-month to one-year intervals by the team.

One day the physical-therapy department received a call from an agency concerning a child who had been evaluated one year earlier. They requested re-evaluation of the child's motor abilities. The therapist immediately informed the executive director, who scheduled the child for complete testing by all departments. After the child had gone home, it was discovered that occupational therapy had been missed because of a misunderstanding on the part of the child's mother. Following this incident a system was developed using a tag listing all the tests necessary. As each department completed its test the list was initialed by the tester. This tag was then returned to the secretary, whose desk was near the door. She could easily see if all the tests had been given, and she also had a record of who did the testing.

A special education class for children was planned for the

summer. Ten children were evaluated by the team and six were chosen. When the associate director called the parents of the selected children, the social worker overheard her talking to Jimmy's mother. As soon as the associate director hung up, the social worker said, "I wish you had discussed this with me before calling Jimmy's mother. She is a very excitable person. I know they will be unable to supply transportation and I doubt if they can afford the tuition."

The associate director replied, "I didn't hear you mention this as we selected the children. It just seems that no matter how hard we try to communicate around here we still have problems! I guess we don't ask each other often enough, 'Exactly what is it you are trying to do?' You are right and Jimmy's mother is quite upset. Before I continue calling the rest of the mothers, are there any other problems I should know about?"

"No, I guess not. It will take a couple of sessions with Jimmy's mother to calm her down and help her understand, but the other mothers will go along with the schedule."

Questions

1. In spite of their efforts to coordinate ideas and facilitate communication, what problems still existed at Meeting Street School?

2. Were some of these problems avoidable? If so, how?

3. Were those problems due to personalities or administrative procedures or both?

References

Barrett, Jean. *The Head Nurse.* New York: Appleton-Century-Crofts, 1962, pp. 38, 41.

Brown, Esther Lucile. *Newer Dimensions of Patient Care,* Part 2. New York: Russell Sage Foundation, 1962, Chap. 4, "Communication and Coordination of Patient Care."

Forsdale, Louis. "Helping Students Observe Processes of Communication," *Teachers College Record*, 67(Nov.): 120–28, 1965.

Geitgey, Doris A. *A Handbook for Head Nurses*. Philadelphia: F. A. Davis, 1962, Chap 2.

McDaniel, Myra L. "Words Are Responsibilities," *American Journal of Occupational Therapy*, 16: 55–60, 1962.

McMurry, Robert N. "Democracy Is What We Strive for, But Autocracy Gets Things Done," *The Modern Hospital*, 90: 52, 1958.

———. "Clear Communications for Chief Executives," *Harvard Business Review*, 43: 131–47, 1965.

Owen, Joseph K. (ed.). *Modern Concepts of Hospital Administration*. Philadelphia: W. B. Saunders Co., 1962, Chap. 49, "Current Trends in Administration."

Urwich, L. *The Elements of Administration*. New York: Harper and Brothers, 1942, pp. 117–18.

Whyte, William H. *Is Anybody Listening?* New York: Simon and Schuster, 1952.

"I can't eat," the patient said when an aide appeared.

"I'll get the nurse right away," the aide said and disappeared.

"I can't eat," the patient began again when the nurse came.

"The head nurse is right here. I'll call her," said the nurse, vanishing into the corridor.

"I can't eat," the patient told the head nurse who replied at once, "The dietitian is here on the floor, and I know she'll be able to help you."

"I can't eat," said the patient to the dietitian at length.

"Why not?" the dietitian asked.

"No silver," said the patient.

Eleanor Lambertsen

From "Looking Around," *The Modern Hospital,* 99: 69, 1962.

Who Does What—And When
—Or Why Don't They!

Blaine Memorial was an overcrowded community hospital. In this small community it was difficult to find an adequate nursing staff or other specialized hospital employees. Consequently all departments had many aides and assistants who were uneducated townspeople whom the hospital employees had trained to do various specialized types of work.

Under these circumstances the director of nursing service, Miss Buckman, struggled with the following problems. Under her direct supervision came the head nurses for each floor, the practical nurses, the orderlies, and the men and women who cleaned the patients' rooms.

Visiting the patients on Ward B, Miss Buckman noticed that all the windowsills were grimy with dust and soot. There were rings where flower vases had been removed, and wilting flowers, long since a cheering sight, drooped for lack of water in the hot afternoon sun that streamed through the window. She went into the hall to search for a cleaning woman. Coming upon a woman with a mop she said, "Would you please clean the windowsills and water the flowers in Ward B?"

223

The woman replied, "I'll do it, ma'am, but it's not my job. I get paid to keep the floor clean."

Somewhat surprised Miss Buckman asked, "Whose job do you think it is?"

"The nurses' aides, ma'am, it's their job to keep the windowsills clean."

Wishing to be cooperative, Miss Buckman excused herself and looked about for the pink uniform that designated the nursing aide. Finding one, she asked once more, "Would you please clean the windowsills and water the flowers in Ward B?"

The aide looked surprised, but said, "Yes, ma'am," and started in the direction of Ward B.

Miss Buckman then went to the head nurse on the floor and inquired, "Whose responsibility is it to clean the windowsills and water the flowers?"

The answer was, "The student nurses should water and rearrange the flowers, and the cleaning lady should dust the windowsills."

Miss Buckman's next visit was to the floor devoted to private and semiprivate patients. She found herself caught up in the rush to get supper served. She was amazed at the confusion she observed. Nurses, aides, and orderlies all combined their efforts to deliver the trays as rapidly as possible to the patients. However, before the trays were delivered, lights began to appear in almost every room. The nurses began to answer the lights. In Room 10 the patient, a Catholic, had ordered fish and received beef stew. In Room 5 the patient had no silver. In Room 2 a very ill patient complained, "All I want is a cup of tea. I have everything on my tray but no tea."

Miss Buckman heard the nurse admonish, after a quick check, "You didn't mark tea on your menu. How do you expect to get tea if you don't order it? Now I'll have to make you some myself."

In Room 7 a patient, blinded by accident two days previously, had a tray but could not feed herself. She had "heard" her supper arrive but it was left just out of reach. Miss Buckman arrived in time to see a maid pick up the tray and begin to remove it, saying to the patient, "My! My! You didn't eat a thing! Aren't you hungry?"

The patient replied, "Yes, I'm hungry, but I couldn't find the tray."

As Miss Buckman fed the patient, she wondered who would have done so had she not happened by.

Because of these interruptions many patients received their supper cold, and many others endured eating what they had not ordered or ate whatever they could, making the best of it. Once again Miss Buckman sought out the head nurse to ask why such confusion existed.

"It's all the fault of the dietetics department," the head nurse said. "The trays come up incomplete or with the name plates switched."

Miss Buckman sought out the dietitian in charge. As she approached, she heard her say to a teen-aged girl placing a tray on a cart, "No! No! Katherine, Mrs. Whitley's tray goes on the next cart marked Ward C."

Miss Buckman decided that this was no time to discuss the problem, but waited until the following day after all breakfast trays were served. She explained to the dietitian the extra work caused by errors in the dietetics department. Further consultation brought out the fact that aside from the dietitian, there was no professional help. Because of low salaries there was a rapid turnover of employees. Training them in addition to planning the general hospital menus and special-diet menus was more than one dietitian could do.

On her way back to her office Miss Buckman passed a room from which paroxysmal coughing could be heard. She heard two passing nurses say, "Who's that coughing?" but they made no effort to enter the room. Seeing equipment outside the door that would relieve the coughing, she took it into the room and brought immediate relief to the patient. Miss Buckman noticed the untouched breakfast and asked the patient if she would like to eat. The patient said she would like a cup of hot coffee. Since the coffee on the tray was cold, Miss Buckman said she would make some hot coffee. The patient looked surprised and said they had told her when she first started coughing and asked for hot coffee that she would have to wait until the breakfast trays came up.

After she had cared for the patient, Miss Buckman sought the head nurse, the only registered nurse on the floor. The head nurse had gone to the coffee shop for a break. Miss Buckman asked one of the practical nurses why the coughing patient had been ignored. The practical nurse said she did not know how to use the equipment and that this was not her responsibility. Miss Buckman found the head nurse in the coffee shop and asked her why she had taken a coffee break, leaving the floor with the coughing patient uncared for. The head nurse replied that the doctor had left the equipment but had left no order for its use. She asked why the patient had not, at least, been given a cup of coffee when she asked for it when the coughing first began. The head nurse showed surprise and said that the patient most certainly could have had it, but that it must have been an aide who refused it, probably because she was too busy to stop and fix it.

Miss Buckman returned to her office realizing that some of these problems could be solved by better personnel policies, but she also wondered how these policies could be maintained without more and better qualified personnel.

Questions

1. What were some of the employment problems? Under the circumstances could better qualified workers be found?

2. In spite of the employment and personnel difficulties, what could Miss Buckman do to improve the situation?

3. Who should decide who should clean the windowsills, the head nurse or Miss Buckman?

4. What sort of administrative policies seem to exist (or not exist) among the nursing services?

References

Agnes, Edith A. "Nine Ways to Improve Nursing Service," *The Modern Hospital*, **97**: 112–13, 1961.

American Nurses' Association. *Functions, Standards and Qualifications for Practice.* New York: American Nurses' Association, 10 Columbus Circle, 1963.

Gilgan, Edward W., and Elizabeth Perry. "Where Does the Dietitian Fit in?" *The Modern Hospital*, **85**: 106–8, 1955.

Hartman, Jane. "Everyone Talks about Delegation But It's Easier Said Than Done," *The Modern Hospital*, **98**: 142, 1962.

Howe, Arlene. "Supervisors Coordinate Patient Services," *The Modern Hospital*, **101**: 77–81, 1963.

Lambertsen, Eleanor. *Education for Nursing Leadership.* Philadelphia: J. B. Lippincott Co., 1958, "Evolution of the Nursing Team Concept."

———. "Nurses Role Changes as Hospitals Assume Wider Role in Patient Care," *The Modern Hospital*, **100**: 152, 1963.

Linville, Clifton H., and William R. Hudson, Jr. "We Taught Our Nurses to Become Managers," *The Modern Hospital*, **100**: 96–97, 1963.

Singersen, Fred. "Hospitals Need More Patience with Patients," *The Modern Hospital*, **95**: 79–81, 1960.

Taddis, Wayland McManus. *The Hospital Head Nurse*, 2nd ed. New York: The Macmillan Co., 1944.

Wright, Marion J. *The Improvement of Patient Care.* New York: G. P. Putnam's Sons, 1954.

———. "Small Hospital Questions," *The Modern Hospital*, **95**: 76, 1960.

Can anyone prove who killed Cock Robin?

Who Murdered Mr. Strong?

Riversedge Hospital was a nonprofit general hospital. The administrative atmosphere was democratic. When decisions or changes had to be made, they were discussed and decided upon by all personnel involved.

Mr. Strong was a paraplegic patient who had been shot in the back during a holdup. The wound had caused paralysis of both legs. Mr. Strong's physical therapy prescription was for passive range of motion to both lower extremities. Because he had a cardiac condition the head of his bed was elevated.

When Miss Terry, the physical therapist, arrived at his bedside to treat him, she noticed a shortness of breath and asked him if he felt able to have his treatment. He replied that he did. After treating one lower extremity, Miss Terry became concerned because the patient's color wasn't good. She discontinued the treatment and consulted the patient's private nurse. She then reported to the head of the physical therapy department that she had decided not to finish the treatment because of Mr. Strong's color and breathing difficulty. About three quarters of an hour later Mr. Strong died as the result of an embolism.

Four months later, when the trial of the holdup man came to court, the defending lawyer raised the question that perhaps Mr. Strong's death was caused by Miss Terry's treatment. The lawyer was under the impression that massage had been given and thought this might have produced the embolism.

One of the assistant administrators of the hospital was representing the hospital in court. He asked the physical therapy department for the prescription card, but found that Mr. Strong's record was already being held by the court. Miss Terry reported to him that massage was not prescribed; only passive exercise had been prescribed. The assistant administrator felt that this should be discussed with the hospital director, and a meeting was held immediately between the director, the assistant administrator, and the physical therapist. During this conference the sheriff arrived and served Miss Terry with a summons to go to court. The hospital director was reassuring to Miss Terry. He asked her to tell him exactly what treatment she had given Mr. Strong. When she could not remember just what she had done, he was understanding. Miss Terry asked if she could see Mr. Strong's chart to help her recall the treatment given. The director said the chart was in court, but that he would contact the neurology resident, who was already in court, and have him refer back to the day in question. When this was done, it was found that Miss Terry had written the following treatment into the record:

> Passive motion to both lower extremities.

She had signed it stating,

> Treatment was discontinued after one limb was treated because of the patient's shortness of breath and poor color.

It was not necessary to call Miss Terry into court because the neurology resident was able to clarify the matter at the trial.

Questions

1. What aspects of this case would indicate that extreme legal precautions should be kept in mind?

2. Why would the written records be important in a case of this kind?

3. Did the therapist do the right thing when:

a. she treated the patient?
b. she consulted the nurse?
c. she recorded her treatment?
d. she reported the incident to her department head?

4. Did the assistant administrator handle his responsibilities well?

5. What policies could be established to avoid further confusion in such cases?

References

Baltz, F. L. "Need for Medical Records," *Hospital Management,* 91(March): 6, 1961.

Creighton, Helen. "Law for Physical Therapists," *Physical Therapy Review,* 38: 22–25, 1958.

Dempsey, Mary W. "Physical Therapy Records," *Physical Therapy Review,* 35: 337–39, 1955.

Hayt, L. E. *Legal Guide for American Hospitals.* New York: Hospital Textbook Co., 1940.

Horty, John F. "Courts Set the Pattern for Medical Records," *The Modern Hospital,* 100: 142, 1963.

———. "Records Belong to Hospitals—Not to Patients," *The Modern Hospital,* 101: 102, 1963.

Lesnik, Milton J., and Bernice E. Anderson. *Nursing Practice and the Law,* 2nd ed. Philadelphia: J. B. Lippincott Co., 1955.

Myers, Robert S. "Physician's Signature Needed for Added Legal Protection," *Hospitals,* 94(March): 126–28, 1960.

Owen, Joseph K. (ed.). *Modern Concepts of Hospital Administration.* Philadelphia: W. B. Saunders Co., 1962, pp. 631–33, "Medical Records, Admissibility of Records in Court."

Shindell, Sidney. "Do You Need Malpractice Insurance?" *Physical Therapy Review,* 37: 655–57, 1957.

Thr proplr in our drpartmrnt arr much likr thr krys of a typrwritrr. Wr all work togrthrr in a cooprrativr way. Thrrr is, howrvrr, onr problrm which you may havr alrrady noticrd. Onr kry dors not work at all so somr othrr kry has to rrplacr it. Although this dors not stop all thr othrr krys from working it mrans that somronr rlsr works twicr as hard and rvrn thrn things arr not vrry rasy to undrrstand. In othrr words, "onr sour applr can spoil thr wholr barrrl".

Admission Chaos

Mrs. Styvesant was a wealthy widow who lived in a small town in the Middle West. The nearest large medical center was 100 miles away. Her husband had died in the ambulance on his way to this center where better facilities for treatment might have saved him.

When the shock of his sudden death had passed, Mrs. Styvesant visited the hospital administrator, Mr. Katz, and asked what facilities could have saved her husband's life. Mr. Katz suggested she ask Dr. Crump, who was her husband's surgeon. Dr. Crump explained the necessary equipment to Mr. Katz and Mrs. Styvesant.

"How much would that cost?" asked Mrs. Styvesant.

"About $20,000," said Dr. Crump.

"How often would you use it?"

"Oh, at least once a month and often once or twice a week."

Mrs. Styvesant turned to Mr. Katz, saying, "Order it and send the bill to me."

"Thank you very much!" exclaimed Dr. Crump and Mr. Katz.

Mrs. Styvesant continued, "I have no immediate dependents so I won't need the money. Several lives might be lost each year owing to lack of facilities. In the future I hope you will let me know some of the needs of the hospital. I will help in any way that I can."

"There just happens to be an opening on our board of directors," said Mr. Katz. "Would you like to be a member of our board? In that way you would be in constant touch with our problems. Not all of them are financial, and I'm sure someone with your interest would be a great help to us."

"That would also keep me busy, now that my husband is gone," replied Mrs. Styvesant. "I'd like that very much."

"I'll see how soon it can be arranged and let you know," said Mr. Katz.

"I'd also like to arrange to endow the hospital in any way you feel the money could be used. I plan to will all I have to this hospital so that future townspeople will feel secure and well cared for medically."

"We'll work that out through our board of directors in the near future," agreed Mr. Katz.

Mrs. Styvesant soon became a board member and continued to give generously of her time and money. Several years passed and Mr. Katz grew to depend a great deal on Mrs. Styvesant's support. A feeling of friendship and gratitude developed among all who knew of her constant interest and support. Finally, as a surprise to her, the hospital was renamed "The Roy J. Styvesant Memorial Hospital."

One day Mr. Katz picked up the phone to hear Dr. Crump say, "Mrs. Styvesant just left my office. There may be a malignancy and I advised her to come into the hospital immediately for further examination. I thought you should know. It doesn't really look too good and I'm very concerned that we may be too late even with immediate surgery."

"I'm sorry to hear that," said Mr. Katz. "Thank you for letting me know." He started for the admitting office to meet Mrs. Styvesant personally, but before he got to the door the chief engineer entered. He was concerned because there seemed to be a large crack in the concrete floor underneath one of the boilers. This discussion took quite some time and involved Mr. Katz's going directly to the boiler room to see what had to be done. When he returned to his office some time later, his phone was ringing. It was a nurse on the third floor who said, "Mr. Katz, I think you should come up here right away."

"What's up?" asked Mr. Katz.

"It's Mrs. Styvesant."

"What's she doing on third floor? She should be in a private room."

"That's just it. She's been assigned to Room 305."

"Room 305!" cried Mr. Katz. "I'll be right up!"

Room 305 was the hospital's only "security room" for prisoners or psychotic patients. The door locked automatically upon being closed and could be opened only from the outside. The windows and all lights were covered with heavy screening. There were no mirrors and no equipment with which anyone could injure himself. Mr. Katz arrived to find Mrs. Styvesant in hysterics. "Dr. Crump is afraid I'll try to do away with myself," she sobbed to Mr. Katz. "Why else would I be put in this room? Can't you assure Dr. Crump that he can trust me no matter how bad things look? I trust him to do the best he can. I don't like it in this room."

Mr. Katz promised to take care of the matter immediately. He first called Dr. Crump to see if he had ordered it. Dr. Crump was astonished. "Heavens no!" he exclaimed, "I never thought of such a thing. Put her in a private room immediately!" Mr. Katz went to the top floor to arrange the transfer, but he found that all the private rooms were occupied. Distraught, he went to the admitting office to find out why Mrs. Styvesant had been put in Room 305 in the first place. On the way he recalled previous incidents when Mrs. Moriority, the admissions clerk, had placed people whom she felt belonged to the "social set" in the hospital's worst accommodations. He also recalled an incident when she insisted a patient with a herniated disc sit down while she filled out his admitting papers. The patient had repeated three times that he could not sit down owing to his injury. Mrs. Moriority had become angry stating, "How can I make out your admission forms if you won't sit here and give me the answers?"

Another time it seemed that she deliberately took longer than necessary in admitting a pregnant mother about to deliver her baby.

On another occasion a patient came rushing up to her with

blood spurting from a wrist, which was obviously badly cut. "I'm sorry," she said. "You'll have to go around to the emergency room. We can't take care of you here."

"Where is that?" asked the nervous patient.

"Out the front door and follow the road to your right around to the back of the hospital."

Mr. Katz had heard about this because special help had been requested to clean up the trail of blood leading to the emergency room. He stormed into the admitting office, saying, "Don't tell me you didn't know who Mrs. Roy J. Styvesant was!"

Mrs. Moriority showed surprise. "Well," she bristled defensively. "She insisted on a private room. 305 was the only one available."

"Mrs. Moriority, this time you have gone too far. You know very well that Room 305 is our security room. Did you explain *that* to Mrs. Styvesant?"

"No, Mr. Katz, but there really are no other private rooms."

"I haven't time now to discuss this further, but please come to my office tomorrow morning," said Mr. Katz. "You cannot remain in this position as admissions clerk any longer."

Mr. Katz returned to Room 305 to find Mrs. Styvesant even more upset than before. "I was unhappy enough to think Dr. Crump didn't trust me! Now the nurses have told me it is all a mistake. I want at least another private room. I want at least a phone in my room and a television set."

"But Mrs. Styvesant, there are no other private rooms. Would you accept a semiprivate room?" asked Mr. Katz.

"No, I would not, Mr. Katz! Under the circumstances I wish to be taken to the medical center in the next town before it's too late, as it was for my husband. I would also like to see my lawyer immediately since I plan to change my will!"

Mr. Katz tried his best to reassure Mrs. Styvesant. He realized that she had plenty of cause to be upset, and he tried to remain calm. "Mrs. Styvesant, after all you have done for us, please let us take care of you. A private room will be ready just as soon as one of the patients can be moved. In the meantime we'll be sure to have a phone in here and a television set and a mirror. I assure you that we'll be sure to give you every possible service."

Somewhat reassured, Mrs. Styvesant agreed that if the door to her room was fixed so that she could go in and out at will, and if she were provided with a phone and television set immediately, she would be patient until another room was found.

Since there was no jack for a telephone in Room 305, Mr. Katz arranged with the telephone company to run a wire over the roof from the opposite side of the wing. He asked the maintenance department to change the lock on the door and to install a television set. He did not go home until he saw for himself that Mrs. Styvesant had every convenience they could provide under the circumstances. Dr. Crump went to assure her he had not been the instigator of this unpleasant situation.

Questions

1. What policies or procedures could have avoided most of Mrs. Styvesant's problems?

2. Whose fault was it (*really*) that Mrs. Styvesant was placed in Room 305?

3. Who, along her path of admission, could have avoided the incident?

4. What alternatives could have been suggested or explained to Mrs. Styvesant rather than simply assigning her to Room 305?

5. Did Mr. Katz fulfill his responsibilities as hospital administrator?

References

Brown, Esther Lucile. *Newer Dimensions of Patient Care.* New York: Russell Sage Foundation, 1961, Chap. 4, "Receiving the Patient into the Hospital."

Georgopoulos, Basil S., and Floyd C. Mann. *The Community General Hospital.* New York: The Macmillan Co., 1962, Chap. 3, "The People Around the Patient."

Owen, Joseph K. (ed.). *Modern Concepts of Hospital Administration.* Philadelphia: W. B. Saunders Co., 1962, Chap. 11, "Admitting."

Urwick, L. *The Elements of Administration.* New York: Harper and Brothers, 1942, pp. 117–18.

Parents are a problem!
or
What to do with the old folks?

Medicare Implications

Mrs. Dvorak, who was 80 years old, lived with her 90-year-old husband in an old house on the outskirts of a small community in New England. Their only income was social security, but since their house was fully paid for and neither drove a car they lived in relative comfort.

Their son, Bill, aged 55, had recently retired owing to a back injury. He lived with his wife, Indra, who was working as a secretary. They lived nearby and assured the older couple companionship, grocery shopping, and any necessary transportation. They also served as interpreters since Mr. and Mrs. Dvorak spoke very little English.

As it does so often with the speed and unexpectedness of lightning, Mrs. Dvorak suffered a cerebral hemorrhage. Mr. Dvorak called his son Bill. Bill called the local physician, Dr. Brown, who reported that he could not make a house call until after office hours but promised to visit Mrs. Dvorak that evening. Dr. Brown gave suggestions as to her care until he could get there, advising the family to keep her quiet in bed. Since Bill could do no lifting because of his back injury, Indra was called home from work to help care for her stricken mother-in-law.

When Dr. Brown finally arrived, he found Mrs. Dvorak with signs of complete left hemiplegia, dazed, confused, and euphoric. He called the hospital and asked to have his patient admitted only to be told there would be no room for several days. Because Mrs. Dvorak was in a completely disabled condition Dr. Brown suggested that the family contact the Public Health

Nursing Association to provide emergency care until Mrs. Dvorak could be hospitalized. He indicated that there was little hope of recovery to the point where Mrs. Dvorak could care for the house and her husband. Owing to the expected need for long-term care Dr. Brown explained to Indra and Bill the basic plan of Title XVIII of the Social Security Act. He explained that after three or more days of hospitalization Mrs. Dvorak was eligible for up to 100 days of extended-care services in a qualified nursing home. He pointed out that although Mr. Dvorak did not want it, they were eligible for 100 visits—such as by a visiting nurse.[1]

Mr. Dvorak totally rejected the idea of an "outsider" helping them and insisted that "the family" could take care of itself. Two other sons, Joe from West Virginia and Charlie only 30 miles away, were contacted.

Charlie came immediately and was predominantly concerned about his parents' financial status. He suggested to his father that the house be signed over to him so that they could qualify for welfare assistance. Mr. and Mrs. Dvorak had no bank accounts but had hidden an unknown amount of money about the house. Charlie suggested all money be given to him and he in return would handle all financial affairs.

A family argument ensued, but both Mr. and Mrs. Dvorak (who was still confused) insisted that all financial affairs be left to Charlie.

While waiting for Mrs. Dvorak to be hospitalized, Bill and Indra carried the burdens of caring for both Mr. and Mrs. Dvorak. Indra continued to work, but this involved getting up at 5 A.M. to be sure her mother- and father-in-law were fed and cared for. Charlie and his wife appeared spasmodically to see how things were going but seldom stayed long enough to give the extended care necessary to bathe, feed, and dress Mrs. Dvorak.

When the time came for Mrs. Dvorak to be moved to the

[1] Frank W. Reynolds and Paul C. Barsam. *Adult Health*. New York: The Macmillan Co., London: Collier-Macmillan, Limited, 1967, p. 197.

hospital, she refused to leave her home. She was enjoying all the attention she was getting from her children and entered the hospital only on the insistence of Dr. Brown.

She was finally settled in a high hospital bed with no side bars. Before the night was over, thinking that she was still at home, she rolled out of bed and fell, fracturing two ribs. In spite of this, Mrs. Dvorak continued to remain euphoric and soon learned to enjoy being waited upon by the many people who attended her bedside. The food was better than she had been used to at home and she ate ravenously.

When the required three days of hospitalization had been completed, Mrs. Dvorak was reluctant to leave the hospital and did not want to be sent to the extended-care facility. Again, it was only under the firm advice of Dr. Brown that she finally agreed to transfer.

In the meantime Mr. Dvorak was unable to care for the house and cook for himself. He still refused any "outsiders"; so Bill and Indra continued to care for him.

Once again Mrs. Dvorak adjusted rather quickly to her new environment. She noticed that other patients wore nylon stockings and fancy silk slips and wanted her daughter-in-law to buy her new clothes. She enjoyed having lots of people around her, and although she spoke little English, she made many friends. In fact, when her Medicare coverage expired, another family crisis arose. Charlie did not want to pay for his mother's continued care, and Indra and Bill did not see how they could continue to care for both of the old folks at home.

Joe was called upon and left his employment to come up and see what could be done to help solve the situation. Joe and his wife finally agreed to take both Mr. and Mrs. Dvorak home to West Virginia. Mr. Dvorak was willing to go with Joe but Mrs. Dvorak wanted her husband to join her at the extended-care facility. A long argument ensued and it was finally agreed that Mr. Dvorak would go home with Joe.

Charlie would continue to pay his mother's expenses in an extended-care facility if Indra and Bill would visit her often. They promised to see that she got the many small items she wanted to keep her happy in an environment discovered through illness.

Questions

1. What are some of the socioeconomic implications involved with Mr. and Mrs. Dvorak?

2. What might become of Mrs. Dvorak if Charlie eventually uses all of her money and possibly all of his and is unable to keep her in a nursing home?

3. Does Medicare give adequate financial assistance to someone in Mrs. Dvorak's permanently disabled condition?

4. How much longer might Mrs. Dvorak live needing expensive medical attention?

5. Does the coming of Medicare imply that the United States is leaning toward socialized medicine?

6. Was Charlie right (legally) in believing that if all property was given to him his parents could go on welfare?

References

American Physical Therapy Association. "Medicare and Physical Therapists," *Physical Therapy*, 46: 768, 1966.

Reynolds, Frank W., and Paul C. Barsam. *Adult Health*. New York: The Macmillan Co., 1967, pp. 197–98.

Social Security Administration, U.S. Dept. of Health, Education, and Welfare. *HIM-1, Conditions of Participation for Hospitals*. Washington, D.C.: U.S. Government Printing Office, 1966.

———. *HIM-2, Conditions of Participation for Home Health Agencies*. Washington, D.C.: U.S. Government Printing Office, 1966.

————. *HIM-3, Conditions of Participation for Extended Care Facilities.* Washington, D.C.: U.S. Government Printing Office, 1966.

————. *HIM-4, Conditions for Coverage of Services of Independent Laboratories.* Washington, D.C.: U.S. Government Printing Office, 1966.

————. *Principles of Reimbursement for Provider Costs.* Washington, D.C.: U.S. Government Printing Office, 1967.

————. *Health Insurance Under Social Security.* Washington, D.C.: U.S. Government Printing Office, 1966.

Summary

Having read the cases that illustrate many of the problems faced by administrators, it is obvious that "the best laid schemes o' mice an' men Gang aft agley." [1] Administration in the medical environment has problems that differ greatly from those of administration in industry or education. Dealing with critically ill patients presents the ever-present need for changing policies to meet immediate problems. Strong policies prevent suffering and provide good patient care with cooperation of all employees working together with integrity and good human relations.

LEADERSHIP IS NEEDED

Because of the many emergencies that arise, strong and accurate decisions need to be made by well-educated leaders in all departments. All department heads need to work cooperatively in order to accomplish common goals for the welfare of the patients. Under these circumstances good leadership and a thorough understanding of administrators and their responsibilities are essential.

[1] Robert Burns. *To a Mouse. A Book of English Literature.* Edited by Franklyn Bliss Snyder and Robert Grant Martin. New York: The Macmillan Co., 1935, p. 779.

ALL EMPLOYEES MUST UNDERSTAND ADMINISTRATION

Employees in the medical environment must first understand the role of administration. This should be part of their orientation to their own special job. Each institution should have a printed organization chart, and every employee should know to whom he is directly responsible. Through understanding the functions of administration all employees will then be ready to support their administrator by assuming their own responsibilities.

THE HOSPITAL ADMINISTRATOR AS MIDDLEMAN

The hierarchical structure of most medical institutions and the real necessity for doctors to give orders that delegate functions to an ever-increasing number of medical and technical groups tend to maintain an autocratic atmosphere in medical administration. This is emphasized repeatedly in the cases. The confusion that often results between the hospital administrator's role as business administrator and also coordinator of policies of the medical staff has also been demonstrated.

Through various patterns of organization each administrator strives for the best professional relations between all departments. He makes the most integrated use of equipment, space, and skilled people, for the care of sick patients. In so doing he stands as middleman between the board of directors and the medical staff. His assistant administrators make many decisions that relieve him of minutiae. His primary role is to hold his leaders together, coordinate their activities, and lay foundations for future trends. He needs time to study changing trends in medical care and to prepare the physical plant and staff to meet the newest and best methods of patient care.

OTHER PEOPLE HAVE ADMINISTRATIVE RESPONSIBILITIES

The above is also true of all employees with administrative responsibilities. They must keep their administrator aware of the need for new equipment or new methods of patient care. All administrators have a legal, moral, and ethical responsibility to the patient to assure him at all times the best medical care. Congenial human relations, both *intra-* and *inter*departmental, are important to the patient's peace of mind, sense of security, and early recovery.

ETHICAL, MORAL, AND LEGAL DECISIONS

All employees have times when they are in doubt as to whether their actions are ethically, morally, or legally right. One can only stay close to those truths which seem morally right and good for the patient. This often takes courage and inner strength and involves personal sacrifices in the interest of the best possible patient care. Although all employees are constantly making ethical decisions at all levels of employment, it is the responsibility of administrators to be the guide in making decisions, for the ultimate responsibility rests with the department head or the doctor who has given the original orders.

LEGAL RESPONSIBILITIES

Administrators are responsible for seeing that employees are aware of and abide by the law. The purpose of the law is to promote the general good by protecting the individuals, groups, or state, and vice versa. Unfortunately, people are becoming more "suit"-conscious, and therefore all employees must be aware that they are individually responsible for their actions. Since hospitals are dealing with sick or injured people, accidents can easily occur. Personality and good interpersonal relations are therefore important. By not emotionally aggravating the patient personnel can minimize the possibility of legal complications.

PERSONALITY IS IMPORTANT

Personality is often as important as knowledge and skill. Inability to work smoothly is more likely to result in friction leading to loss of a job than is the lack of knowledge or skill. The personality needed to work in the medical environment requires strength of character and self-assurance. Many of the cases illustrate unwillingness to assume responsibility for errors and mistakes or a tendency to pass the blame to another person with weak excuses.

Since the inner self constantly strives for self-actualization, and the central core of the individual is delicate and subtle, it can be easily overcome by environmental pressure. The individual must hesitate and evaluate his inner self to assure growth with every experience in order to reach his highest notch of discernment. Self-acceptance, knowing one's strengths and weaknesses, and being able to defend what one believes in are essential to all who work in the medical environment, for only through knowing one's *self* can true understanding of patients and co-workers be accomplished.

True peacefulness of soul will reflect itself through responsiveness toward patients. Such strength of character comes from loving and forgiving one's self. Many people work in hospitals because they have a deep feeling of identification, sympathy, and affection for mankind as a whole. As such they want a feeling of belonging, of being useful. Most young people begin a new position with some apprehension. The stronger their orientation in administration, the less this apprehension will be. The more mature the employee is to begin with, the more clearly will he understand the role of the administrator.

NEW EMPLOYEES NEED PATIENCE

New employees should understand that it may take a year or more before they truly understand their organization and its administration. They would be wise to withhold criticism until they are sure they have all the facts. Favorable responses from new employees would include an inquiring mind, offering suggestions, taking time and having patience to understand the total problem, and continuing to seek peaceful solutions without being critical of the present. Administrators behave as they do because they are responsible for seeing that the organization gets the job done with the best human relations possible. As the cases illustrate, this is far from easy and the new employee often cannot understand why admininstrators are not perfect.

DISCUSSION OF CASES WILL INCREASE AWARENESS OF COMMON PROBLEMS

Through discussion of the cases in Part II, students' or young employees' attention is focused on what the student needs to know in order to function in his position. The discussion of these cases will encourage independent thinking and help one to realize as he listens to other people's different opinions that there are many ways to arrive at the best solution for complex problems. This should lead to carry-over into methods of *discussing* conflicts of opinion without becoming emotional about it and lessening personal involvement.

Carefully built into these cases are the most persistent problems existing in the medical environment today. In this way all people using this material can "see themselves" and at the same time see the situation as an onlooker, thereby increasing objectivity. By so doing a greater understanding of administration and administrators should be accomplished.

The purpose of this book is to contribute toward improvement of existing professional relations in the medical environment.

Bibliography

BOOKS

American College of Hospital Administration and American Hospital Association. *Code of Ethics.* Chicago: American Hospital Association, 1964.

American Hospital Association. *Hospital Accreditation References.* Chicago: American Hospital Association, 1964.

American Hospital Association and National League of Nursing Education. *Hospital Nursing Service Manual.* New York: National League of Nursing Education, 1950.

American Management Association. *Effective Communication on the Job, A Guide to Employee Communication for Supervisors and Executives.* New York: American Management Association, 1956.

American Nurses' Association. *Statement of Functions and Qualifications for Nursing Service Administrators.* New York: American Nurses' Association, August, 1966.

American Occupational Therapy Association. *Occupational Therapy Handbook.* New York: American Occupational Therapy Association, 1965.

Averill, Lawrence, and Florence Kempf. *Psychology Applied to Nursing.* Philadelphia: W. B. Saunders Co., 1951.

Barabas, Mary Helen. *Contemporary Head Nursing.* New York: The Macmillan Co., 1962.

Barrett, Jean. *The Head Nurse.* New York: Appleton-Century-Crofts, 1962, pp. 38, 41.

Bash, Wendell H., and F. K. Berrien. *Human Relations—Comments and Cases.* New York: Harper and Brothers, 1957.

Bellows, R. M. *Psychology of Personnel in Business and Industry.* New York: Prentice-Hall, Inc., 1955.

Bird, Brian. *Talking With Patients.* Philadelphia: J. B. Lippincott Co., 1955.

Black, Henry C. *Black's Law Dictionary.* St. Paul: West Publishing Co., 1933.

Brown, Esther Lucile. *Newer Dimensions of Patient Care,* Part I. New York: Russell Sage Foundation, 1961.

———. *Newer Dimensions of Patient Care,* Part 2. New York: Russell Sage Foundation, 1962.

Brown, Milon. *Conference Leaders' Guide to Effective Supervision.* New York: The Macmillan Co., 1956.

Burling, Temple, Lentz, Edith M., and Wilson, Robert N. *The Give and Take in Hospitals. A Study of Human Organization in Hospitals.* New York: G. P. Putnam's Sons, 1956.

Burns, Robert. *To a Mouse. A Book of English Literature.* Edited by Franklyn Bliss Snyder, and Robert Grant Martin. New York: The Macmillan Co., 1935.

Cabot, Richard. *The Meaning of Right and Wrong.* New York: The Macmillan Co., 1933.

Calender, Tiny M. *Unit Administration.* Philadelphia: W. B. Saunders Co., 1962.

Chamberlain, Neil. *Management in Motion.* New Haven: Labor and Management Center, Yale University, 1950.

Cooper, Alfred M. *How to Supervise People,* 3rd ed. New York: McGraw-Hill Book Co., Inc., 1957.

Creighton, Helen. *Law Every Nurse Should Know.* Philadelphia: W. B. Saunders Co., 1962.

Crow, Alice, and Lester D. Crow. *Understanding Interrelations in Nursing.* New York: The Macmillan Co., 1961.

Davis, Fred (ed.). *The Nursing Profession.* New York: John Wiley and Sons, Inc., 1966.

Department of Hospital Nursing, National League for Nursing.

The Head Nurse at Work. New York: National League for Nursing, 1953.

Dimock, M. E. *The Executive in Action.* New York: Harper and Brothers, 1945.

Dooher, Joseph M. (ed.). *Effective Communication on the Job.* New York: American Management Association, 1956.

Etzioni, Amitai. *Modern Organizations.* Englewood Cliffs, New Jersey: Prentice-Hall, Inc., 1964.

Famularo, J. S. *Supervisors in Action.* New York: McGraw-Hill Book Co., Inc., 1961.

Faxon, Nathaniel W. *The Hospital in Contemporary Life.* Cambridge: Harvard University Press, 1949.

Finer, Herman. *Administration and the Nursing Service.* New York: The Macmillan Co., 1952.

Fivars, Grace, and Doris Gosnell. *Nursing Evaluation: The Problem and the Process.* New York: The Macmillan Co., 1966.

Freidson, Eliot (ed.). *The Hospital in Modern Society.* New York: The Free Press of Glencoe, 1963.

Gallagher, Anna Helen. *Educational Administration in Nursing.* New York: The Macmillan Co., 1965.

Geitgey, Doris A. *A Handbook for Head Nurses.* Philadelphia: F. A. Davis Co., 1962.

Georgopoulos, Basil S., and Floyd C. Mann. *The Community General Hospital.* New York: The Macmillan Co., 1962.

Gibran, Kahlil. *The Prophet.* New York: Alfred A. Knopf, 1960.

Goffman, E. "Characteristics of Total Institutions," in Stein, M. R., A. J. Vidich, and D. M. White (eds.). *Identity and Anxiety: Survival of the Person in Mass Society.* New York: Free Press of Glencoe, 1960.

Gulick, Luther, and Lyndall Urwick (eds.). *Papers on the Science of Administration.* New York: Institute of Public Administration, 1937.

Hayt, L. E. *Legal Guide for American Hospitals.* New York: Hospital Textbook Co., 1940.

Henderson, Virginia. *The Nature of Nursing.* New York: The Macmillan Co., 1966.

Hungate, Thad L. *Management in Higher Education*. New York: Bureau of Publications, Teachers College, Columbia University, 1964.

Huxley, Laura Archera. *You Are Not the Target*. New York: Farrar, Straus and Co., 1963.

Jackson, Laura G. *Hospital and Community*. New York: The Macmillan Co., 1964.

Jensen, Deborah M. (ed.). *Ward Administration*. St. Louis: C. V. Mosby Co., 1952.

———. *Nursing Service in Administration*. St. Louis: C. V. Mosby Co., 1962.

Jung, Carl G. *The Undiscovered Self*. New York: The New American Library of World Literature, 1959.

Kelly, Cordelia W. *Dimensions of Professional Nursing*. New York: The Macmillan Co., 1962.

Lambertsen, Eleanor. *Education for Nursing Leadership*. Philadelphia: J. B. Lippincott Co., 1958.

Lesnik, Milton J., and Bernice E. Anderson. *Nursing Practice and the Law,* 2nd ed. Philadelphia: J. B. Lippincott Co., 1955.

Lingren, Henry C. *The Art of Human Relations*. New York: Hermitage House, Inc., 1953.

Lockerly, Florence. *Communication for Nurses*. St. Louis: C. V. Mosby Co., 1958.

Maslow, A. H. *Motivation and Personality*. New York: Harper and Brothers, 1954.

———. *The Self: Exploration in Personal Growth*. New York: Harper and Brothers, 1956.

Merriam-Webster. *Webster's New College Dictionary*. Springfield, Massachusetts: G. and C. Merriam Co., 1953.

Millett, John D. *The Academic Community*. New York: McGraw-Hill Book Co., Inc., 1962.

Moore, Dom Thomas V. *Principles of Ethics*. Philadelphia: J. B. Lippincott Co., 1943.

Morrison, Luella J., and Mary A. Farris. *Approaches for Co-workers in Professional Nursing*. St. Louis: C. V. Mosby Co., 1962.

Moss, Arthur B., Wayne G. Broehl, Jr., Robert H. Guest, and

John W. Hennessey, Jr. *Hospital Policy Decisions.* New York: G. P. Putnam's Sons, 1966.

Nadler, Leonard. *Leadership on the Job, Guides to Good Supervision.* New York: American Management Association, 1954.

National Industrial Conference Board. *Studies in Personnel Policy, No. 129: Communicating with Employees.* New York: National Industrial Conference Board, Inc., (n.d.).

Owen, Joseph K. (ed.). *Modern Concepts of Hospital Administration.* Philadelphia: W. B. Saunders Co., 1963.

Perrodin, Cecilia M. *Supervision of Nursing Service Personnel.* New York: The Macmillan Co., 1954.

Peterson, Wilfred A. *The Art of Living.* New York: Simon and Schuster, 1961.

Public Health Service, U.S. Department of Health, Education and Welfare. *Administrative Aspects of Hospital Central Medical and Surgical Supply Services.* Washington, D.C.: U.S. Government Printing Office, 1966.

Raths, Louis E., and Anna P. Burrell. *Do's and Don'ts of the Needs of Theory.* Bronxville, New York: Modern Education Service, 1951.

Ray, Marie Beynon. *The Importance of Feeling Inferior.* New York: Harper and Brothers, 1957.

Redfield, Charles E. *Communication in Management.* Chicago: University of Chicago Press, 1954.

Regan, Louis J. *Doctor and Patient and the Law,* 3rd ed. St. Louis: C. V. Mosby Co., 1956.

Reynolds, Frank W., and Paul C. Barsam. *Adult Health.* New York: The Macmillan Co., 1967.

Rozos, E. John. *Leadership on the Job, Guides to Good Supervision.* New York: American Management Association, 1954.

Seidenfeld, M. A. *Psychological Aspects of Medical Care.* American Lecture Series, Publication No. 44. Springfield, Illinois: Charles C Thomas, 1949.

Simon, Herbert A. *Administrative Behavior.* New York: The Macmillan Co., 1958.

Sloan, Raymond P. *This Hospital Business of Ours.* New York: G. P. Putnam's Sons, 1952.

———. *Today's Hospital.* New York: Harper and Row, 1966.

Smith, T. V., and William Debbins. *Constructive Ethics.* Englewood Cliffs, New Jersey: Prentice-Hall, Inc., 1948.

Social Security Administration, U.S. Department of Health, Education and Welfare. *HIM-1, Conditions of Participation for Hospitals.* Washington, D.C.: U.S. Government Printing Office, 1966.

———. *HIM-2, Conditions of Participation for Home Health Agencies.* Washington, D.C.: U.S. Government Printing Office, 1966.

———. *HIM-3, Conditions of Participation for Extended Care Facilities.* Washington, D.C.: U.S. Government Printing Office, 1966.

———. *HIM-4, Conditions for Coverage of Services of Independent Laboratories.* Washington, D.C.: U.S. Government Printing Office, 1966.

Social Security Administration, U.S. Department of Health, Education and Welfare. *HIM-5, Principles of Reimbursement for Provider Costs.* Washington, D.C.: U.S. Government Printing Office, 1967.

———. *Health Insurance Under Social Security.* Washington, D.C.: U.S. Government Printing Office, 1966.

Soltonstall, Robert. *Human Relations in Administration.* New York: McGraw-Hill Book Co., Inc., 1959.

Taddis, Wayland McManus. *The Hospital Head Nurse,* 2nd ed. New York: The Macmillan Co., 1944.

Tead, Ordway. *The Art of Administration.* New York: McGraw-Hill Book Co., Inc., 1951.

Urwich, L. *The Elements of Administration.* New York: Harper and Brothers, 1942.

Voeks, Virginia. *On Becoming an Educated Person.* Philadelphia: W. B. Saunders Co., 1959.

Whyte, William H. *Is Anybody Listening?* New York: Simon and Schuster, 1952.

Wright, Marion J. *The Improvement of Patient Care.* New York: G. P. Putnam's Sons, 1954.

PERIODICALS

"Administrative Resident Learns by Listening" (editorial), *The Modern Hospital*, 98: 95, 1962.

Agnes, Edith A. "Nine Ways to Improve Nursing Service," *The Modern Hospital*, 97: 112, 1961.

American Physical Therapy Association. "Medicare and Physical Therapists," *Physical Therapy*, 46: 768, 1966.

Armstrong, R. W. "Empathy," *Nursing Times*, 52: 1006, 1956.

Baltz, F. L. "Need for Medical Records," *Hospital Management*, 91: 6, 1961.

Bird, Brian. "The Nurse Is the Patient's Interpreter," *The Modern Hospital*, 84: 51–54, 1955.

Bluemel, C. S. "Ethics and Public Relations. The Physician's Responsibility to Patients and to Himself," *Rocky Mountain Medical Journal*, 58: 32–36, 1961.

Blum, Richard H. "Good Organization Means Fewer Law Suits," *The Modern Hospital*, 91 (Oct.): 59–62, 1958.

Boettcher, Ernest M. "How to Make a 'Fire-Safe' Hospital Safer," *The Modern Hospital*, 101: 83, 1963.

Brackett, Mary E. "What Nurses Dislike about Their Jobs," *The Modern Hospital*, 89: 53–58, 1957.

Broderick, Thomas J. "How to Help Supervisors Evaluate Employees," *The Modern Hospital*, 95: 89–93, 1960.

Brown, Amy Frances. "Organization of Clinical Learning Experiences," *Nursing Outlook*, 5: 97, 1957.

The Covington News, Andalusia, Alabama, December 18, 1947. Quoted in Albert Lepawsky, *Administration: The Art and Science of Organization and Management.* New York: Alfred A. Knopf, 1960.

Creighton, Helen. "Law for Physical Therapists," *Physical Therapy Review*, 38: 22, 93, 165, 251, 1958.

Davis, Harry A. "Let One Person Do All the Purchasing," *The Modern Hospital*, 101: 14, 1963.

Dempsey, Mary W. "Physical Therapy Records," *Physical Therapy Review*, **35**: 337–39, 1955.

Forsdale, Louis. "Helping Students Observe Processes of Communication," *Teachers College Record*, **67** (Nov.): 120–28, 1965.

Frank, L. K. "Interprofessional Communication," *American Journal of Public Health*, **51**: 1798, 1961.

Freedman, Milton. "Effective Group Relations," *Physical Therapy Review*, **36**: 231–33, 1956.

George, Gordon. "Doctor-Patient Relationships," *America*, **90**: 12–16, 1952.

Gilgan, Edward W., and Elizabeth Perry. "Where Does the Dietitian Fit in?" *The Modern Hospital*, **85**: 106, 1955.

Hale, Thomas, Jr., "Why the Nursing Supply Is Failing to Meet the Demand," *The Modern Hospital*, **95**: 100–4, 1960.

Hartman, Jane. "Everyone Talks about Delegation But It's Easier Said Than Done," *The Modern Hospital*, **98**: 142, 1962.

Heneman, Harlow J. "Administrators Waste Time Chasing Details," *The Modern Hospital*, **99**: 87, 1962.

Hershey, Nathan. "Hospitals' Expanding Responsibility," *American Journal of Nursing*, **66**: 1546–47, 1966.

Hickey, Helen. "A Kit of Tools," *Physical Therapy Review*, **31** (April): 135–38, 1951.

Horty, John F. "Courts Set the Pattern for Medical Records," *The Modern Hospital*, **100**: 142, 1963.

———. "Records Belong to Hospitals—Not to Patients," *The Modern Hospital*, **101**: 102, 1963.

Howard, S. Kenneth, and F. C. LeRocker. "What Decisions Do Trustees Actually Make?" *The Modern Hospital*, **94**: 83, 1960.

Howe, Arlene. "Supervisors Coordinate Patient Services," *The Modern Hospital*, **101**: 77–81, 1963.

Kolb, Mary Elizabeth. "The Challenge of Success," *Physical Therapy*, **46**: 1159, 1966.

Komaiko, J. K. "The Fine Art of Listening," *Parents Magazine*, **36**: 40–41, 1961.

Lambertson, Eleanor. "Looking Around," *The Modern Hospital*, **99**: 69, 1962.

————. "Nurse's Role Changes as Hospitals Assume Wider Role in Patient Care." *The Modern Hospital*, 100: 152, 1963.

Larrabee, Eric. "Who Gets the Message?" *Vogue*, 137: 165, 1961.

Lawshe, C. H., and Nagle, Bryant F. "Productivity and Attitude Toward Supervisor," *Journal of Applied Psychology*, 38: 159–62, 1953.

Linville, Clifton H., and William R. Hudson, Jr. "We Taught Our Nurses How to Become Managers," *The Modern Hospital*, 100: 96–97, 1963.

McDaniel, Myra L. "Words Are Responsibilities," *American Journal of Occupational Therapy*, 26: 55–60, 1962.

McGrath, Robert. "To Fight Fire—First Conquer Fear," *The Modern Hospital*, 85: 58–61, 1955.

McMurry, Robert N. "Democracy Is What We Strive for, But Autocracy Gets Things Done," *The Modern Hospital*, 90 (April): 52, 1958.

————. "Clear Communications for Chief Executives," *Harvard Business Review*, 43: 131–47, 1965.

Martin, Charles M. "Eight Ways to Get Along with Doctors," *The Modern Hospital*, 95: 63–64, 1960.

Masur, Jack. "Top Brass Should Follow the Golden Rule," *The Modern Hospital*, 95: 79–83, 1960.

Monaco, Anthony. "Our Biggest Hurdle Was Tradition," *The Modern Hospital*, 95: 98–99, 1960.

Myers, Robert S. "Physician's Signature Needed for Added Legal Protection," *Hospitals*, 94 (March): 126–28, 1960.

Nadler, Leonard. "A Manager's Job Is to Help Employees Grow," *The Modern Hospital*, 95: 119, 1960.

————. "Small Hospital Questions," *The Modern Hospital*, 95: 76, 1960.

Platon, Carl. "How to Make Friends with People Before They're Patients," *The Modern Hospital*, 95: 112, 1960.

Rossell, Eve. "Human Relations Principles Are the Hospital's Principal Problem," *The Modern Hospital*, 80: 62–64, 1953.

Rozos, E. John. "Everybody Should Have a Part in the Budget," *The Modern Hospital*, 91: 87–90, 1958.

Schlesinger, Lawrence E. "Staff Tensions and Needed Skills in Staff-Patient Interactions," *Rehabilitation Literature,* **24**: 362, 1963.

Shindell, Sidney. "Do You Need Malpractice Insurance?" *Physical Therapy Review,* **37**: 655–57, 1957.

Sigmond, Robert M. "What Utilization Committees Taught Us," *The Modern Hospital,* **100**: 67–71, 1963.

Singersen, Fred. "Hospitals Need More Patience with Patients," *The Modern Hospital,* **95**: 79–81, 1960.

"Traffic Flow Keeps Patients out of the Public Eye" (editorial), *The Modern Hospital,* **95**: 115–18, 1960.

Viguers, Richard T. "What It Takes to be a Good Supervisor," *The Modern Hospital,* **91**: 63–66, 1958.

————. "Building a Hospital Communications Network," *Hospitals,* **16**: 48–51, 1962.

Wright, Marion J. "Small Hospital Questions," *The Modern Hospital,* **95**: 76, 1960.

Yancey, Donna. "Without Words," *American Journal of Nursing,* **62**: 118–19, 1962.

UNPUBLISHED MATERIAL

Beard, Esther Alice. *Toward Understanding People: A Study of the Insights and Goals of College Students Preparing to Teach.* New York: Teachers College, Columbia University, 1959. (Mimeographed dissertation.)

Index